I return

Were you ever inspired
by a dream?

John Kynge

The Legend
of
Castle Winswood

John Kynge

Prairie Orange Management Limited
United Kingdom

First published in Great Britian in 2013
by Prairie Orange Management Limited
Hackney Park, Mount Pleasant Lane,
Lymington, SO41 8LS
United Kingdom
Website: http://www.castlewinswood.co.uk

ISBN 978-0-9574892-0-2

Printed in Great Britain by
TJ International Ltd, Padstow, Cornwall

MIX
Paper from
responsible sources
FSC
www.fsc.org
FSC® C013056

Table of Contents

Preface

After completing my degree in 1997 I had a cocktail of ideas to work on, all with some family or political reference. By 2008 I had enough ideas for a drink, a drink spiked with prairie orange, that American mid-west tree sent back by Lewis and Clark to Washington DC, the spiky barrier that's 'horse high, bull strong, hog tight'!

I was using it as a password; a musical formed in my mind, I wrote some songs and a password management website also appeared as an idea. What if the greeter disappeared? She would be called Alice. Wonderland's Alice had fallen down a rabbit hole, passing a jar of orange marmalade that must have been the first pass word! My website would be in Cornwall. I could imagine Greg Noll in his trademark black and white swim suit surfing the waves of Tintagel; Greg would be a Wall Street index trader searching for Alice.

I travelled down to Kilkhampton; my family appear in the earliest parish registers of 1545, and when I reached the castle mound my cocktail spilled. On the mound in an oak glade I took a picture; I had no idea that the photo when developed would set in motion events that would require me to write the legend of Castle Winswood.

First I found a woman's face in the photo and close by a headless body formed as if extruded from tree branches. Was a virus in control of me? I had a password, the sleeping beauty was awake and I could pass through the great hedge that curtained the castle. But would the castle engage with me and deliver its secrets?

In 2009 I travelled down to the castle again. On a stormy night I had a dream that shook me to the core. Two barbarians in a red cavern beneath the castle mound fed a prisoner's hand to a beast. The following morning I walked the castle trail up from the beach. On top of the first stronghold a buzzard delivered a greeting, circling and calling continuously! I called back, 'I have returned.' My camera and video recorded our meeting, but it wasn't until I reached what I call the corridor of death that unease and trepidation returned. A spring oozing water crossed the path and the trickle was the colour of blood. Something truly terrible had happened here, I was sure. Adrenaline kicked in – my first view of Winswood. I had a password, I was ready for the challenge, I would soon be able to enter the sleeping beauty's castle and tell the tale. A libation had been poured, someone had spiked the drink, all that was left was to take a sip, just a sip like Alice. I had taken a sip and this is what I saw.

Introduction

Why a mind, body and spirit book?

In 1993 as a mature student I commenced a four-year degree course in German at the University of Southampton. As part of that course in the 1995/6 term I studied abroad living in Zurich and attending lectures at the C.G. Jung Institute in readiness for the submission of a dissertation. I read widely in the library of the Institute and I read about the horse. The position of the horse as a psychic intermediary amongst tribal cultures became of particular interest. I read about a US Plains Indian tribe called the Lakota, part of the Sioux nation. I was intrigued by the importance that tribe placed upon the vision quest and the re-enactment of visions in front of the tribe. I learned about their Heyoka.

This mind, body and spirit production follows the re-enactment tradition of the Lakota. My unusual experience commenced with a visit to a castle site in Kilkhampton, Cornwall in 2008 and ended with a frightening dream on another visit in 2009. This text completes part of the requirement demanded of me: describing the legend of Castle Winswood. Only when the legend is filmed will I be released from my obligations.

This has been my first channelling experience. Did I receive personal information? Yes I did. Was I energised by the channelling experience? Yes, immensely. Have all the secrets been uncovered? I am certain that further secrets from this site remain to be uncovered. 'Channelling' is an expression that I have used to describe receiving information, an unusual discovery that causes the recipient to undertake a quest, a search to gain knowledge and in Lakota tradition to relay the information received. How have I dealt with later interceptions and embellishments? I have tried to resist any contamination of the original message.

I hope that this book will deliver advantage and become an inspiration for readers to undertake their own channelling experience by investigating sites like that at Castle Winswood, Cornwall, the source of my own channelling inspiration.

Why is it written in the form of a novella? Goethe demands of the novella that it contain an incredible event. Consider if you were a spirit operating from a fifth dimension and you wished to coerce a writer to engage in your complaint. How would you accomplish the task? You could manage his photo images, influence his dreams, accord him an attachment to a scolding hawk and finally discolour a spring with the colour of human blood – would that sequence engage the writer to share the complaint? What if finally the trail you laid for the writer led to a monstrous crime – an incredible event?

The legend I have recorded starts with a fictional eighth-century Irish maiden's curse on an infamous castle. Could she be the lost girl reproduced in the photo I took on top of a castle mound in 2008? She is certainly a focussing symbol, perhaps a psychic meeting point, a destination, a place where folk can share a suffering. Yet I had no idea that the trail she would lead me along would scare me in a dream where eighth-century barbarians fed a prisoner's hand to a beast! Nor that it would then subject me to a scolding 2009 castle hawk and lead me to a monstrous historical crime, an injustice. If you cut off the heads of 4,500 persons in a single day in response to a tribe's failure to convert to Christianity, would that be an incredible event?

'I have returned,' I cried out to the buzzard. 'I have returned.'

I have returned to tell the story.

Dedication

To my family in England and North America

I should add that I had no knowledge of my connection to the American plains until 1997 when I contacted a Canadian genealogist and Professor of Chemistry at the University of Saskatchewan, Evelyn Jonescu nee Ching, who had written a book upon the Ching family of Devon and Cornwall. The small Devon village of Woolfardisworthy near Clovelly and Kilkhampton was a crucial link that connected our families. I sent to Evelyn a copy of the first page in a family bible that I had inherited. To my astonishment Evelyn informed me that she had found some Chings in South Dakota. These Chings were my direct cousins, being descendants of the Hugh Ching recorded on the first page of my bible. Hugh had emigrated to the USA from Winbrook farm, Kelly in Devon in 1878. My grandfather had never mentioned his uncle farming out on the plains and we still don't know what happened to Hugh's older brother John who was the first to venture to the USA. As a child I had opened an atlas and been intrigued by a small picture of a whirling Great Plains tornado, Evelyn made me aware that I had good reason to have been intrigued by this symbol of danger and turbulence in the American mid-west. 'It's a long way South Dakota' is a song I wrote in appreciation of Evelyn's discovery of my American family. Even odder was to find that my cousins lived in a small town called Castlewood, South Dakota; how's that for psychic resonance?

Prologue

Dark Age Justice

Nudging the blunted edge of the eighth century,
Germanic followers of pagan gods once numerous
Agitate at the tribal root;
Knotted tangles were traced, pursued, subdued.
The Irminsul, a giant tree, an ancient forest shrine
Long worshipped by German tribes
Was but a distant memory –
Dismissed with wood smoke.
Teutoburg Chatti had all converted,
Their famed smoky rings
Suffering the wildest of all pledges
Discard for a forest floor.

Across the land a great Christian king rode stirrup proud
Brandishing a Frank sword he denounced all pagan worship.
Only in Verden, some Saxons refused to honour and pay tribute,
Pagan they would remain.
Yet earlier a Cornish duke in 776 AD honoured their tribe,
Arriving in pomp to marry the young Gisela,
Sailing her hundreds of miles home with her sacred blue horses –
A dowry for Castle Winswood.

By 782 the Verden Saxons so enraged King Karl he vowed to
    loosen heads –
Axes chopped 4,500 for failure to convert!
The river Aller bled, and bled, until its red stream soured the
    Weser,
Only Thor's lightning strike on axeman and pagan girl halted
    the slaughter.

She, Petra survived,
Her back illuminating a protective lattice
Scorning Thor's lick of anger.
Karl's axeman disappeared – Karl's Christian arbiter just a
     smudge of smoke …

In Cornwall the Duke circled
Meeting his king at Bodmin to wrestle threats from Saxon, Irish,
And crow.
In the Duke's absence Duchess Gisela dispensed justice
Bending her ear to hawk and horse.
On Henna cliff the guilty fell
On dragons' teeth.
Beach crabs clattered to share a raven's feast,
The Welsh and their Gower wurm auditioned,
Ryd mouthed his displeasure.

Ryd,
People's champion, twice winner of the great Kylgh horse race
A circle race five miles round
Round the ring at Winswood, Ryd was favourite.
But this his third year a bad sign;
A soothsayer had warned, warned of the angry Duchess,
His vision: a corridor choking with death – summer of 798 –
He'd heard a cry, a ransom girl exciting her tribe to arms,
'They return,' she shrieked, 'Winswood a curse on you,'
Gold pieces lay alongside dragons' teeth.

Ryd's father acted,
Scurrying through green corridors, past buzzard sentinels, he
     put his son to sea
Lundy-bound to meet a summer ship
Laden with gold, Welsh gold for Rome.
And as oarsmen pulled through ocean surf
Duke's port and forgemen spied the father spurring north

Over granite cliffs past green rush and Henna's ravens.
Until far beyond a yellow moor there was a sign
Cihtric gasped,
'To the waterfall of tears.'

At last sight of treasure island and perhaps a glimpse of Ryd's
    tiny craft.
Fifty-foot freshwater mists spray your eyes here
And Lundy Island just ten miles distant
Appears and disappears
In each cloud
In each puff.
Cihtric heard the chink of coins and with a sorrowful look
    beyond the fall
He heard an oracle's questioning voice,
'Ring or beast?
'What did you see?'

Part 1

The Hawk, the Horse, the Ring and the Beast

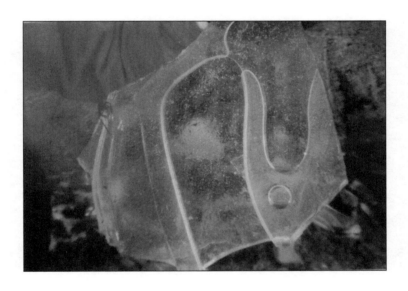

*One clan custom that took place
Involved selecting on a frosty January morning
A blade of ice from a woodland pool.
This blade of ice was read by the clan reader
Seeking to probe into the future.*

The Great Circle Horse Race – Kilkhampton, Cornwall, August 798 AD

Gisela, Duchess of Cornwall, took her hawk from its cage; she moved across the castle room like white foam surfing the tide, frothing, plotting, before slipping the liquid's grasp. 'Ryd,' she hissed, 'find him.' The bird, accustomed to her command, released its grip upon her gauntlet the moment the open window was offered. Like hot lamp wax drifting through a watery element, the bird completed a series of intricate manoeuvres spiralling and threading the castle lands as far as the Duke's port – three miles down the Coombe River to the roaring sea. The Duchess with a quick flick of her finger checked the forward movement of her steel-blonde hair and swept back frowning towards a table where a black-robed figure sat hunched, concentrating on a spill of vision water.

'What summer treasure do you seek, Duchess?' asked the Reader, attentive to the return of the Duchess.

'Treasure? I seek a champion, my champion. I want to win my race! Return to your vision search, Reader, declare who will win; you can do that, can't you?' prickled the Duchess.

'I saw three of your horses together, I saw them clash in the market,' replied the Reader.

'But Ryd, where was Ryd?' the Duchess shouted.

'Ryd, ah … our town's reigning champion,' said the Reader with a nod. 'I just saw dust, he was a long way ahead of the others.'

'And Rannard, where was Rannard?' the Duchess asked, fearing that none of her four horses would defeat Ryd in the great circle race to be held on the following day, the August feast day to celebrate summer's success.

'I saw Rannard with a blade in him, a blade right through his body,' confirmed the Reader.

'Ah,' screamed the Duchess, clawing the air, 'my champion!'

'And, at the river,' continued the Reader, 'some of your men were standing knee deep in water but Ryd was nowhere to be seen. Sword blades pooling in water; he must have evaded them.'

'Never,' cried the Duchess. 'But you didn't see Ryd with the feather – the golden feather to be awarded the champion – my golden feather?' Not waiting for the Reader's reply, the Duchess circled the table where the Reader had purposely spilled the vision water.

'Again, again, commence the vision again,' urged the Duchess, returning to her seat beside the Reader.

The old man pressed his hand into the water and fixed his gaze upon tiny droplets that lay in the triangle of his upturned palm. 'Our flags have unfurled, a woman wagers on Ryd for victory! The sun is high, all five riders are ready, and they are off! I hear shouts and the deafening call of the carnyx! Your blue horse banners flutter over the castle walls.'

The Duchess remained silent, listening intently.

The old man continued, 'The great crowd beside the treasure hill throw marking spears towards the riders to ward them away from the castle. And Ryd leaves the group. He charges at the crowd, he seeks to shortcut the racers, to beat them to the front of the castle. Instead of anger, they flee, they applaud, he is their champion, I hear shouts – Ryd for champion!'

'Ryd will never be champion again,' countered the Duchess, shaking her head. 'Now where are you?'

'In the market square. Ryd is cheered through the street, far in front of your laggards, and now they enter the square, there is a crush, lots of screaming. A slam, a slice, they are trailing in Ryd's dust. I see them all out on the Clovelly road riding north, north for Lundy Isle and a sight of Wales.'

The Duchess nodded. 'And now my blue horses will catch Ryd,' she asserted.

'No, he's too far in front, at the crossroads I see him turning west for Raven's Crag. The fork for the Henna cliff and the sea road face him and four horses are still spaced out in his wake!'

'Ah, is there no one who can stop him?' exclaimed the Duchess, springing up. 'He is a splinter in my side, he challenges my laws. Why, if it wasn't for the Duke, I would have had my talons in him years ago.' The Duchess beat her hand on the table, making her fingers into a claw, disturbing the pooled water. Her dwarf Lucco, who had been listening intently beside the table, jumped in fright.

'He rides on past the sea road fork at Stursdon. I trace him turning south, returning on this half-circle stretch leading to the southwest cleft. It's narrow at Lee, his horse falters, they are catching him, they are catching him,' reported the Reader.

'Rannard will catch him,' the Duchess said excitedly, 'my blue horses will stay this distance, Ryd's steed will slow.' The Duchess closed on the Reader, who was looking down, focussing past his hand into the vision water.

'Ryd's steed is sure of foot and he enters the cleft 600 yards east of the corridor of death and ... I've lost him, I cannot see him, he's shielded behind the great oaks.'

'And now an arrow through the trees,' suggested the Duchess in spiteful humour, her eyes glancing quickly at Lucco, who drew closer to the tabletop.

'I see your horses in the cleft, one has fallen. I hear screams, another is down, who will reach the water first? I still cannot see Ryd. But ... yes, yes, I see him in water, he has reached water and in front of your men, he cannot be stopped,' the Reader asserted.

'Aahh, he must be stopped,' the Duchess shrieked, 'I will not have him winning my race. Where are my guards? Enough of this!' She turned from the table, shaking with rage, and hurled her hawk gauntlet across the floor.

'My lady,' gasped the Reader.

'Yes, Reader?'

'Your guards have put a blade into Rannard. It's Rannard who has fallen.'

'Get out of here.' The Duchess still trembled with rage; her voice rose again. 'It will not happen! Mark me! We will find Ryd tonight. There will be no race for Ryd, no golden feather, no five miles of fame, no adulation. It will not happen, do you hear? The Duke is in Bodmin, I will take charge!'

'Duchess Gisela.' The Reader hesitated, dipping his head.

Scowling, the Duchess nodded at Lucco, who produced a small pouch and commenced to withdraw some coins. 'Did you see the woman's face?' she asked the Reader.

'The woman who wagered upon Ryd?' queried the Reader. This woman had opened the Reader's visual diary. The Reader looked directly back at the Duchess. 'Yes,' he replied, 'I did see her face; it was Ryd's mother, Cihtric's wife,' and his hand crossed swiftly to pick up the coins that the dwarf began counting out.

'A mistle's trotter, a smolt's tousel, a fly's tongue,' the dwarf muttered, and he looked up as the last of the three coins was accepted.

'Vespasian,' remarked the Reader, holding out the last coin.

'To remind you of the great circle race,' declared the Duchess.

That night the Duchess's mood darkened, a violent summer storm struck Castle Winswood, and by daylight

Rannard the Duchess's champion was found dead in the stables, a blade driven right through his body – there was no sign of Ryd.

No one could find Ryd since Ryd's father Cihtric had taken his eldest son that very night and despatched him from the Duke's port to Lundy Island, onward bound for Wales and Carmarthen. It was true the Reader hadn't seen Ryd hold high the golden feather for a third time. Ryd would not ride in the great circle race of 798 AD at Kylgh. The people of Kilkhampton and the circle had lost their champion.

Shipwreck on the Moroccan Gold Coast

The storm that engulfed the gold convoy continued for three days. By the end of the first day the two gold galleys were nowhere to be seen and the four Viking escort ships had been flung far to the south of Gibraltar. They bobbed away in pairs until this bleak unity was broken. By the third day, scanning the angry horizon, Ryd had found no hint of any sister ships, they were alone and the storm that had raged through the night beckoned again. On the fourth day their proud ship was beaten and broken; the dragon prow slipped beneath the waves, taking all the crew with her except for three men whom Neptune rejected. These three clinging to wreckage were Ryd, Ingvar the 'kenntsman' and Cai.

As dawn peeled back across a bright blue sky, these survivors lashed themselves to a cross spar still carrying the tattered remnants of their sail and its emblem, a proud Viking hawk. Alongside the spar could be seen a birdcage where two crows, black and wet from spray, occupied a central position. These crows with their black beaks had survived. Of the three Viking seamen – although Ryd could hardly be called a Viking, hailing from Castle Winswood in Cornwall, and Cai a native of Welsh Carmarthen whence the gold convoy had departed for Rome just two weeks before – only Ingvar had experience of surviving a shipwreck. Ryd's father, a commander at Castle Winswood, the feared North Cornwall dragon castle, had despatched his oldest son on the pretext of learning seamanship and passage skills through the Mediterranean, and here was Ryd learning from Ingvar how to respond to shipwreck.

'Watch the cage, watch the cage,' shouted Ingvar; 'if we lose these black-feathered beauties who will direct us to the African shore?'

Cai nodded; he and Ryd had failed to secure a second cage to the spar. The image of that birdcage coiling down through the water continued to pain Ryd, who was knowledgeable on the Greek god Poseidon and his Roman counterpart Neptune. The birds' whitened beaks and eyes in alarm had fed snaking lines down to the depths where the water god and tentacles had secured the birds. Athena wouldn't help, concluded Ryd, whose pagan beliefs held fear in check as he gripped the spar and clenched his teeth at each trammelling from white horses, surfing wave heads, chasing his eyes. Cai was unconcerned with bird loss – they were Welsh rooks, he mouthed; their eyes had no knowledge of the Moroccan gold coast!

What do you grab when your vessel lurches towards the depths? Doesn't every sailor have a plan? Grab a sword, a flag, a sign, a firing flint, water gourd, caged bird? Maybe a biscuit? Ingvar had known his flints were in his pocket, so his first sword thrust had hacked at the sailcloth that would provide him with shelter, then had come the water gourd and the caged birds, which he had lashed to the free spar. He stroked another blade that nestled tightly in his belt; he had been overboard before, he knew they would have little time to survive in these seas, but so long as they could reach a beach, there was a chance, so long as he could find the biscuit! Ryd, seeing him grab the birds, had followed suit, grabbing a cage and grasping a leather gourd; he too felt for the biscuit hidden inside his tunic and the strike blade hidden in his boot that would fire his flints.

*

And they survived; through the African surf, off a dangerous cape on the Gold Coast of Morocco, the three sailors in pursuit of their crows found land. The crows had flown east. They were nowhere to be seen. They had fled the wrecking coast. Fled the beach of bones.

The sailors applauded their good luck except for Cai, whose leg had been shattered by a falling spar. He held back a cry as the two able men hauled him up the beach above high water. Ingvar laid out all their possessions and advised the men of his plans. They did not include dragging Cai's weakened body back to the sea, drowning him and then stretching his carcass across the fire. But a day after their arrival on the beach, that was what happened.

Cai knew the seriousness of his injuries. 'Your father won't forgive me, I promised to protect you,' said the ailing seaman, 'to keep you from Winswood, away from the Duchess!'

'We reached the beach; that is enough,' said Ryd. 'The Duchess cannot chase me here.'

'Aye,' acknowledged Cai, 'and now come hard choices; we have little water. Listen to Ingvar, Ryd, and obey him; he will find the way home.'

'And you, Cai, what of you?' asked Ryd.

'This wound has done for me, look, see my skin, see the spots: poison, poison is spreading and the pain swells. Ingvar knows, not even my ring can work a charm for me,' and here Cai rubbed the iron ring that blackened his finger. Ryd squeezed his hand and returned to the fire with wood from the wreck.

During their first night Ingvar whispered to Ryd, 'Can you smell his leg?' Ryd nodded; the flies had pursued Cai all day. 'We can't leave him like this, it hasn't rained, we have too little water for three!' Ingvar shook the sail with its bold hawk symbol. He set it to protect them from sun and capture rainwater if a sudden cloudburst descended on the beach. 'You know what we must do, Ryd, it must be done soon,' threatened Ingvar. Ryd nodded; he had seen men die from battle wounds, and there was no arguing, Cai's leg had become infected. *Kenntsman* means 'the knowledgeable one' and Ryd wouldn't oppose Ingvar's decision.

On the afternoon of the second day Ingvar found Ryd marking the sand after returning from a failed attempt to source fresh water. 'What are you doing, Ryd?' questioned Ingvar.

'When I return I'll have nine judges – see, they will sit here in a line. Here where I've shaped a butterfly the petitioner will face the judges to make his case, supported by the blue bird here. And here the hare – you can stand and be the hare. Now who will direct our judges questions for the defendant? A black cat,' worried Ryd. 'The Duchess, she's even followed me here.'

'And what is that position there?' asked Ingvar, pointing towards a flat stone with seaweed upon it.

'The toad stone; the cat rules the night and the toad the underworld underwater ...' 'Ryd, you need to get a grip,' said Ingvar. 'Tonight at dusk, neither of us found water; it must be tonight, enough of this silliness.'

Ryd skirted the sand behind the nine judges – 'law, and justice,' mouthed Ryd. Ingvar had no knowledge of Ryd's problems with the Duchess.

'There is no law here, Ryd,' said Ingvar. 'Whilst we live, we are the judges; there are no nine judges. We live in a society that is continually at war – what did that Greek call it: "War is the father, the king of all things; some are revealed as gods, some as mere men, some it makes slaves while others remain free!" There is nothing about a cat, a hare or a toad, they can't pay for wars – you need gold!'

'Well, after Cai's gone I will play the butterfly,' remarked Ryd.

'After Cai's gone both of us must beware the Berber hawk,' pronounced Ingvar.

Ryd could only fixate upon the Duchess's hawk; she turned to her hawks and horses for advice on all matters of discontent at Winswood. After sentencing, those found guilty were flung to their deaths from a high Cornish cliff called the Henna cliff. And it was Ryd who had attracted the Duchess's attention and disapproval.

Yet Ingvar was correct; down the beach, to the south from where the survivors had made their fire, a Berber hawk had been urged to scare crows from what looked like carrion. A hunter whistled boldly for his bird to break off its attack. The crows took a moment to organise and then depart; they had survived their first beach challenge. The hunter allowed his hawk to settle upon what looked like a body – remains of a striped hyena's meal. While the hawk inspected the crab-emptied eye sockets the hunter signalled the hawk to return to his gauntlet, rewarding the bird before placing a hood over its head. A decaying body – sure sign of a shipwreck – no doubt more bodies would appear and maybe survivors. The Berber scoured the beach for signs, searching the spray, welcoming the opportunity of a wreck.

Ryd refused to eat from the charred remains. It was the lack of fresh water that had provoked Cai's death march. Ingvar poked at the fire. 'Cai won't need this ring,' he announced, and he sliced the iron ring from Cai's finger. Ingvar flipped it with his blade to Ryd, who poked it around with his own blade before returning it.

'Is it a charm?' Ryd asked.

'It's an old German ring,' said Ingvar. 'I've seen these markings – it fits!' and he set the ring onto the little finger of his right hand. 'And if it were Welsh gold it would be fit for a pope.'

With no point in sharing water with Cai, Ingvar had dragged Cai into the surf through the receding sounds of the tide as it had released its hold on the beach. Ryd had remained immobile by the fire, poking, looking and hoping ... but with that leg injury Cai had had no prospect of survival.

Ryd remembered Cai's last words: 'Ryd, I'll miss the cuckoo, the swallows ...'

'And I'll miss the races, the horse races at Kylgh,' Ryd had interjected, and he had recalled the races instituted by the Duchess to test her sacred Weser bloodlines. 'But I'll miss something deeper. I'll miss the sound of the surf at Signal Point and the bubbling river joining the sea, I'll miss the high trees, the summer airs and the perfume that attracts the insects and I'll miss that first spectacular view of the great castle at Winswood.'

'I'll miss our nightjars,' continued Cai.

'Most of all I'll miss uncovering the secrets of the Tamar's dark soul,' said Ryd, remembering his sight of the devil's cauldron on a tributary river gorge far to the east at Lydford.

'I'll—' Cai had failed to complete the sentence. Ingvar had struck him.

'Your wing was broken,' Ingvar had whispered to the lifeless Cai, dragging the body back through the sand from his mission to the surf.

Ryd had remained sheltering by the fire. He had seen eyes viewing from the dunes, bright shiny eyes: the eyes of a beach witness – a striped hyena.

'The beach hunters would have killed Cai the moment they

saw his wounds. They would have continued slicing just to quench their blades,' advised Ingvar, acting out a slicing fury. 'Now they will see two men, two able men, and they will see slave money – we will live!' And he pointed determinedly at Ryd with his open blade. Ryd shook the contents of the last water gourd and sucked. How long would the water keep this butterfly alive?

And later that same evening the hunters came, criss-crossing the strand; they'd seen the smoke and just as the hawk's eye in the sky scans for carrion, so they found the two survivors sheltering under sailcloth. Bells on the horse saddles alerted Ryd to the first hunter, but Ryd was far too weak to offer any resistance. The hawk glared. The two white men were given water and roped together. The hunters dug in the fire, noting the charred limbs; smiling, they turned for their camp, prisoners wrapped in sailcloth kafiyehs: an eye for Ryd and talons for Ingvar.

It was hours before the women and children spilled into view, smells of charcoal and fish swept the beach, darkened smoke, laughing, and the tents of the Berbers appeared in the dunes. The eyes of the striped hyena scanning the beach melted into Ryd's memory, tagging his mournful trek.

They were fed. The two men shuffled closer to a family fire where on the perimeter children were using sticks to agitate two scorpions. Ryd watched mesmerised. 'What are these?' He tugged at Ingvar.

'Why do you think they use sticks?' returned Ingvar.

'I don't know,' said Ryd, and he went to poke at one with his finger.

'Stop!' shouted Ingvar, and pulling on the rope that lashed them together he jumped onto the two scorpions, grinding them to death. 'This is a dark continent, Ryd,' pronounced Ingvar. 'If something is in your space kill it! Don't play with it and never become mesmerised by it!'

The Berber children giggled, their eyes glinting in the firelight.

'Saved for slavery,' Ingvar whispered at Ryd. Ryd forced a smile in the flickering light. Twice he had turned on the trek hours before to view Cai's fire. The beach hunters had heaped sand and smothered dying embers. A smell had lingered. Ryd's first African scars: shipwreck, an accusing finger, eyes viewing white lives – animals' eyes.

Slave Auction at Sijilmasa

The wind stirred the Saharan sand in eddies as the salt caravan from Idjil carved its way north, hundreds of miles from Fez. It was late in the evening and five of the beach hunters accompanying their two white prisoners had joined this Berber caravan of animals and men.

Ryd could hardly believe his eyes; what were these beasts? He had never seen anything like them before. Much taller than a man, they could carry far greater loads than any horse. They stretched out in a line far into the distance. One passed blowing out what seemed to be a red bladder through its mouth, and it lathered and spat in Ryd's direction. Why, it even seemed to have fangs. Ryd resolved to give these animals a wide berth, yet he wanted to learn more about these creatures peculiar to the tribes of the desert.

The blade that woke Ryd later that night pricked his jaw on the right jowl of his unshaven face. He feared the urgency of the awakening and his hand came up to defend himself. He murmured, 'Uh!'

Wide awake, he moved to rise and was met with the resistance of the same blade pressing hard against his vertebrae. He iced over; his face returned to the sand. His thoughts raced. Was he roped to Ingvar? Was Ingvar still asleep? The knife bit into his back, forcing its way through the cloth. The slightest movement on Ryd's part brought renewed anxiety from the blade, each stirring of complaint answered by the blade pressing deeper. What was Ryd to do? Would the blade carry on its excursion down his back or with one sudden sharp movement pierce his body? Fear engulfed Ryd; he stayed absolutely motionless, hoping the pricking of the blade would stop. The interrogation continued. Ryd was sure some design had been drawn, yet he was too frightened to attempt any move; the fewer his complaints the less animated the reaction of the blade. Ryd obeyed its movement and remained still, glued to the sand. He wanted to give a great shriek, pull on the rope, wake Ingvar and turn on his attacker. But he could do nothing, he had yielded his territory, yielded his part of the sky. Covered in sweat he feared the thrust. He had an overwhelming urge to relieve himself. *Help me, help me*, the only thought wracking his brain.

And then as if by magic the blade ceased its wandering, it left his back. He heard no sound; he inhaled and gave out a gasp of relief. He was shaking. He was wet. He turned over and he raked his back on the sand bar. A sharp pain met his exertions; he had not imagined this steel interlude; he had been attacked, and he had been injured. He was probably bleeding. Would the blade return? He took great gulps of air and resolved to stay on his back listening. The blade must have drawn a map. How close – death? His tongue moved in his mouth, now wet with saliva. He swallowed; he was wet over his loins; he peered into the dunes and he thought he caught the glint of eyes staring. A collision had occurred. He had been marked forever. Yet perhaps this had been his opportunity to escape, to pull at Ingvar and race into the dunes. But with what? They had no water, no food. They would be walking a road of death. Ryd remained too terrified to let out a scream. To avoid collisions in the beast's corridor you need more than a map.

The journey behind salt-laden camels was slow. The relentless torture of the sun required a halt through the midday hours when temperatures became unbearable. Then to average twenty miles a day the caravan would journey late into the night. As prisoners in the rear, Ingvar and Ryd had just their kafiyehs to protect their nostrils from a choking envelope of flying sand and animal smells. The mounted hunters were eager to leave the salt caravan and cross westwards to the great Taghaza slave road which would bring them, once they turned north, to the notorious trading town of Sijilmasa on the banks of the river Ziz. Large numbers of black slaves travelled this ancient 'trail of tears' from Awdaghust, their bodies pierced, scarred and in chains.

Two days after leaving the salt caravan and crossing to the gold and slave route, an attachment to a northbound Sijilmasa caravan was arranged after discussions with a Berber chieftain. The camels in this train numbered in the thousands. The beasts stretched out in a line that seemed to have no end. The beach hunters appeared happy with the deal they had struck and left returning south.

Ingvar's insistence that he and Ryd were Viking slaves had alerted the beach Berbers. They had responded by checking wrists and ankles for clues. One Berber had jabbed at the blackening ring mark caused by the iron pledge ring on Ingvar's finger. 'Viking slaves,' Ingvar had replied. The Berbers had paused; the ring and the rune markings had attracted their attention, but the reward they could achieve by selling the two white men into slavery dictated their view.

Later Ryd had asked Ingvar why he had taken the ring – after all it wasn't gold. 'It's made of iron,' Ingvar had replied. 'For some it is just a trinket but for me it's magic, it will lead us north, it will always point north. It's our way home!'

Ryd and Ingvar had watched the beach Barb horses disappearing in the distance. The two white men now found themselves amongst hundreds of black slaves, both men and women. Animal cages strapped on the backs of camels held lion cubs, hyenas; there must have been more than a hundred guards; all the prisoners were in chains. The camels all laden with heavy goods formed part of an endless line common to travellers of this hot and empty desert space. What were they carrying? 'Gold, it must be gold,' suggested Ingvar.

The chaining process concluded, the two white men were attached to a large group of female slaves. Ryd scanned the scarring and markings on the black women, who viewed the white men with suspicion and made no attempt to engage in speech. The few female Berbers Ryd had seen back at the beach hunters' camp had had facial markings made from henna but nothing like the scars he now observed upon some of the black slaves. Pointing at one of the black female slaves Ryd exclaimed, 'See her back scarred and marked; do you think it's a recent wound? What can it mean?' He wondered whether his own back had healed from the blade wounds made earlier. He had held back from informing Ingvar. 'What can it mean?' he repeated.

'What do you think it means?' hissed Ingvar, moving closer to the girl. 'It's her way home; they are scarring a map upon her back!'

Shocked, Ryd viewed the scarred back as if expecting some village to yield its name; instead he saw a tiny horse in yellow ochre and what looked like a feeder river. Seeing her wounds, his own wound woke and began to complain. 'I've seen brands upon our sacred blue horses, stars, the moon; if I return I will make my own shield brand,' Ryd said. 'I'll have the sea, a high hawk tree and then our castle tower.'

'Perhaps you would like that design upon your back,' answered Ingvar. 'I could add a beast, or like this slave girl a horse. Her golden horse leads to a city of gold. South it must be, through this vast desert. I've heard traveller's tales of golden horses: sentinels over gold for as many camels as there are stars in the sky!'

'No thanks,' Ryd said, flinching. He understood most pagan signing, but not this new version from the Africans – new signs ... lines scored in blood!

He would always remember Ingvar's finger tracing the map on the girl's back, south, south to a city brimful of African gold, and he would never forget the blackness of Ingvar's eyes as he scolded, 'What use is justice here, Ryd? You need gold to avoid these chains, gold enough for a nobleman's ransom! With gold you can ride through the wildest dream.'

So that was what the blade on Ryd's back provided – a map, perhaps a gold map. But what use is gold in a desert? Arabs treasure their camels and on the caravan train these were the only mounts of the Berbers. The horses were favoured nearer the coastal areas where water was in abundance. There were two types of horse seen by Ryd: the Barb and the Arab. Black or white Arabs were the chosen mounts of the Berber chieftains. There were several watering places along the route; the caravan did not carry excess quantities of water for slaves or animals. Ingvar and Ryd were given a little dried fish at the evening halt.

Despite being far from the Fez road, Ingvar was sure that at Sijilmasa he and Ryd would meet traders from the old Roman town of Volubilis near Fez and there be despatched for the coast and home. Ryd worried about separation from Ingvar, who could navigate by the stars. Ingvar had saved them from certain death on the coast, but would their luck hold at Sijilmasa? This trading settlement had been founded by Iza bin Masid the black; internal struggles within Berber clans had claimed many lives until the town had passed through the Barghawata kings to the present time. Now this eighth-century town was once more strengthening its grip on merchant trading across Moroccan Sahara – north, south, east and west.

Each night as the two white prisoners settled amongst the female slaves it was Ingvar who attempted silent conversation with the nearest female prisoner, marking the sand, moving his hands, searching eyes. Just the clink of rings announced his progress – was he feeling for a map?

On arrival at Sijilmasa, the slaves were washed in the River Ziz before being paraded to the auction site where a great throng of people surrounded the wooden viewing platform. Slaves, then later that day animals would appear in the bidding ring. The auctioneer laughed and joked while the main merchants bid frenziedly against each other. You cannot judge intentions from a casting of faces, concluded Ryd, remembering the auctions at the circle, the Kylgh, at Winswood.

All the black slaves had been auctioned and just the two white men remained. Ingvar with his black hair and swarthy complexion, his darkened hands, the ring; Ryd, flaxen hair, a blue-eyed warrior – what would they bid for them?

The merchants' interest appeared to have waned. Some were admiring their new female slaves. An Arab chief began the bidding for Ingvar. He was sold quickly and that left Ryd. Ryd felt many eyes upon him, eyes dark and suspicious. At this point, unannounced, riders entered the arena. This did not appear part of the auction process. This was a separate show, some entertainment! The crowd hurried to their seats, Ryd was herded towards a cage at the side of the arena and as the horses pushed him closer to the cage he could see an animal, one that he'd never seen the like of before. Later he learnt it was a Barbary lion. The animal's roar sent a wave of terror through his body. Ryd was defenceless. He had no weapon. The animal lashed at him through the bars with its great paw and the horsemen pressed Ryd closer and closer to the cage and the claws. Falling to the arena floor, Ryd scored sand and hurled it at the lion before escaping to the centre of the arena, rolling beneath the horses, avoiding their hooves. The riders were angry at Ryd's quick flight although he showed not an ounce of fear of hoof or whip. Their disapproval was signalled through turning their horses back to face him and raining down a succession of blows upon his head and body.

The northern warrior lusts for challenge and a test of arms, nowhere more so than in Cornwall, land of dragons and giants. The gladiatorial arena was Ryd's domain; this task to overcome riders and lion he would relish. If these desert folk desired entertainment then Ryd would entertain them. Of course it would be a fine balance; Ryd knew that he could not escape, but he needed to play to his strengths, his riding and his bravery. Here were four riders circling him, wishing him to embrace the cage and the lion; if somehow Ryd could gain control of a horse perhaps he could gain the support of part of the crowd just so long as he wasn't disrespectful of all the riders. Somehow he needed to advance the game, up the stakes; what risks could he take? What roles would horse and lion play? There would be no room for error.

His earlier visit to the cage had allowed him to see that the cage could be opened from the arena side. Now he stood up, dusted his outer garment and ran at speed towards the lion. Before he could be stopped he had the bolt drawn and the cage door open. The riders now faced a different quarry. Ryd was behind the gate and moved to a flight of steps cut in the arena wall for the very purpose of effecting an escape after freeing the door. Ryd had the same thing in mind – releasing the animal and moving to a safe spot. Unfortunately the safe spot was barred. The flight of steps out of the arena was unavailable.

The lion, intent on obtaining its freedom, paid no attention to Ryd or his dilemma; it leapt out of its cage into the arena with a great roar, much to the fear and consternation of riders and crowd alike. The beast's claws flashed; riders fled, keeping as far from the beast as possible. The lion advanced on the centre of the arena before changing its mind and charging against the nearest arena wall. The spectators screamed. The barrier held. Those more adventurous closed on the lion from their seats and spat and shouted down on the animal. The riders were shouting for the exit passages to be opened to allow their escape.

Ryd moved from behind the cage and its control gate to attract the beast's attention. A sword was thrown down to him from within the crowd – so someone desired a proper contest! On the other side of the arena three riders were escaping on their mounts when Ryd shouted 'EPONA!' at the top of his voice. The last horse pricked its ears, reared high on its hind legs and threw its rider to the floor. It appeared that Ryd would now be swept aside by the lion in a frenzied attack but the beast had choices: the fallen rider, the horse or Ryd. Before a decision could be made Ryd called to the horse, which promptly raced across the arena and stood before him. The crowd gasped; never had they witnessed such control. The rider lay injured, no chance of escape, and the lion began walking towards him. Ryd mounted the horse. And before the lion could gather speed to pounce on the wounded rider Ryd was galloping directly at the beast, shrieking at the top of his voice and flashing the sword blade.

Ryd passed the lion's hindquarters as the beast lashed out. The horse halted and, raising itself on its own hind legs, flailed out with its hooves. Now the lion would be Ryd's amusement, and far from being frightened Ryd and his steed closed the distance to challenge and instil fear. The lion had no intention of leaving the arena without some victory, and skirting the horse with several bounds it made its intention to circle and pounce on the injured rider. Ryd urged his horse forward with the flat of the blade raised high and brought it down hard on the rump of the roaring lion, causing it to leap away from the injured man. A huge cheer came from the crowd aware that this move had saved the man's life.

Before the fallen rider could be endangered any further a number of guards rushed into the arena and with nets the lion was snared. Ryd dismounted and helped the injured rider to his feet, allowing more guards to tend to the injured man and secure his horse. Ryd patted the animal before walking over to the empty lion cage to be greeted by a merchant.

'An interesting display,' said the merchant, 'but my lion's worth more than a slave, even one as remarkable as you. I have agreed to reimburse the arena for their loss of amusement; usually the slave is dragged to the cage and mauled before being left for the beast. In your case you will leave with me. We depart tomorrow for Saldae. Ah, the sword, it's mine.'

Ryd was surprised but returned the sword to the merchant.

'My friend Ingvar?' asked Ryd.

'He's sold, gone. You won't see him again,' answered the merchant. 'What's your name?' he asked, all the time speaking perfectly in Ryd's tongue.

'Ryd,' Ryd replied, 'and yours?'

'Call me Sijilmasa; it will be easier to pronounce and remind you where we met,' said the Jewish merchant.

'Silmasa, Silm … Silas,' concluded Ryd, and the merchant motioned Ryd to accompany him towards his entourage.

'I am taking you to Saldae,' Silas said. 'There I will sell you to one of the Roman galleys.'

'And my friend?' asked Ryd.

'Do not waste time on your friend.'

'My friend wanted to reach Volubilis.'

'Ah, Volubilis, a fine town, but you will find Saldae much more to your liking, trust me. First some food, and since you have cost me so much money you will be caged for your protection. Trust me, travel with my animals; Sijilmasa is a dangerous town!'

There were four cages: a lion, some apes, a striped hyena and an empty cage chosen for Ryd. 'Enjoy your sleep; you won't come to any harm in there,' said the merchant. 'We leave tomorrow in the afternoon.'

His black security companion was laughing. 'Heh heh heh,' the man grunted as he closed the cage on Ryd, smiling. At least he had been rewarded with amusement.

Warrior slave or slave of the sand? Slaves at Kilkhampton were never killed for amusement. Enemies were killed for amusement and to engender fear of the clan but slaves were too valuable, too important in the moving of goods from port to the castle. Here in the desert there was a great source of slaves to the south, an abundance of slaves, and many of these slaves were the victims of inter-tribal hatred. Just a glance of dissent would be rewarded with death – slaves of the sand were worth less than a gourd of water.

*

So how do you prepare yourself for a long journey through the Atlas all the way to Saldae? Its later name of Bougie meant 'the candle'. You will need water even though your camels can manage for six months without water and pace twenty miles a day. The animals you eat will travel with you, but it is the water that is truly essential to man for a long journey under the harsh rays of the sun. At night you will need a good blanket; it is very cold in the High Atlas at night.

Ryd could observe from all sides of his cage. The heat was unbearable, so the caravan would hold up during the middle of the day and then commence walking from the afternoon until late evening or right through the night. There were over fifty guards with this caravan slowly travelling northeast towards Icosium (Algiers) and Saldae.

On the second day Silas spent time with Ryd and to his surprise Ryd learnt that the merchant had travelled to Britain whilst a young man. He had traded in tin and remembered an island ringed by the sea that at low tide lay connected to the mainland, and he remembered a great river. 'Tamar,' he said.

'Our river,' answered Ryd. 'Winswood lies close to its source.'

Silas beamed. 'You will welcome a return then.'

'Indeed I will,' replied Ryd, 'I miss the river, its mysteries and the land.'

'I have a slave named after your river,' said Silas. 'Perhaps the mysteries of this woman are a fine parallel to those of your river.'

Ryd was a little confused; which slave was Silas talking about? What mysteries did he refer to? Ryd had only heard of those at Eleusis. Ryd decided he would enjoy meeting any woman called Tamar but that would come later, perhaps at Saldae.

*

'May I feed the animals?' ventured Ryd on the third day to Silas. Behind each cage a food compartment had been connected; these animals were worth considerable sums and their wellbeing was important. Silas had no reason to think that Ryd would run off into the desert and, nodding, he turned away from his captive to talk with his guards.

Ryd opened the food box on the hyena's cage and took out a bone; he had seen the guards feed the animal over the last few days. Poking in one piece, he put his hand into the food bin to extract another bone and found that in his hand he held what was clearly a human hand!

Ryd felt an urge to vomit; he looked back at the hand and noticed it was someone's right hand and on the third finger was Ingvar's ring, the ring he had removed from Cai! He clasped the hand to his chest and looked around – was anyone watching? His heart was racing; what had happened to poor Ingvar? Then without further thought Ryd pulled at the ring; he didn't care about any bad omen; he slipped the ring into his boot and threw the human hand to the beast. Abruptly he ended his participation in the animal feeding and returned to his cage.

'I couldn't finish,' he later informed Silas.

'Why?' asked Silas.

'A human hand,' said Ryd.

Silas joined Ryd by the cage. 'I should have told you, the Arabs in Sijilmasa carry out all sorts of retribution. You pagans carry out sacrifice too. So you saw a hand.'

'I saw a hand with a ring, my friend Ingvar's ring,' replied Ryd.

'You are a pagan, aren't you? You will be returning with the galleys. Your friend was unlucky; opponents of Islam are often beheaded here. Your friend was chosen, he stood out, he was wearing a ring; beware, in these lands a ring can bring certain death. The ring is a sign of provocation – I own, I belong, these ideas I uphold. When you are a slave you will *not* have a ring. You are an empty container. You will own absolutely nothing, not even a thought!'

Certain death – the phrase reminded Ryd of the corridor of death at Winswood now that was certain death for everyone, regardless of rings worn on fingers, and what if the Duchess's hawk or horse whispered your name? That too was certain death. In these Moslem lands there was no ambiguity over signage; here a black ring on the finger meant you weren't a slave. Worse, it could mark you out as a Christian, and Christians were beheaded.

'And what about you, Silas?'

'The Arabs they choose to trade, we Jews have traded with them for years. I know I am not safe. A change of ruler, an angry merchant and my life would be forfeit. Do not mourn too much over your friend. Life can be short in the desert. Hope that his death was quick; there are some here who can make death a long, long drawn out matter; there are tortures of which you cannot conceive, but then I am sure you have your own tortures at…'

'Winswood,' pronounced Ryd. 'Castle Winswood.'

And indeed the dragon castle was well known for torture. Ryd composed himself and sat back on his haunches; he was lucky to be alive and Silas's captive! He didn't doubt that there were indescribable tortures here in Africa. For some tribes there would be always be pleasure in protracting the death process, but it was a skill Ryd had no intention of procuring.

Four days out of the trading town riders appeared from the south, brandishing weapons; they halted the caravan. 'You took some carcasses, some bodies, there was a hand,' spoke a mounted warrior seated upon a black Arab stallion.

'I paid for the meat – your men know well, you required its disposal and I paid.'

'Well, our chief remembers the ring and he wants the ring of provocation!' the warrior shouted menacingly.

'The ring – we have fed the beasts, the ring would have been eaten – see for yourselves,' said Silas.

The hunters checked the animal cages and searched through the food bins, finding neither human hand nor ring.

'We will take this slave,' said one retainer, pointing at Ryd.

'And return him when you find the ring,' shouted the hunter on the black Arab. He dismounted and moved towards the cage containing Ryd.

The caravan guards now joined their merchant leader in a protective circle.

'Why a white slave? I have many others,' said Silas, pointing to distant camels carrying other members of his entourage with their black slaves. 'Besides,' he added, 'this slave has already been sold, promised in Icosium. The wrath of Allah would be upon me if I were to grant you this man. Consider the danger that would befall us.'

The hunter flinched; he had no wish to precipitate a struggle that could cost him his head. The slave was already promised; he could not break the bargain.

'If the ring appears then keep it for me and on your return you will be rewarded. Our leader had a dream and in the vision he saw the ring again, saw the markings. These markings attracted his attention!'

'We will find the ring if Allah so wishes,' replied Silas. Turning, he signed for the caravan to continue. The hunters disappeared in the dust.

And suddenly Ryd was reminded of Cai and the storm. On the ship he had heard Cai talking and sealing with the ring against his palm:

> *This ring*
> *Resounding under sea mist gibbet*
> *Scorning every mew gull's claw*
> *Embered in a single blacksmith's thrust*
> *Offers neither ebb nor break through fame or threat*
> *The tide awakened*
> *Reminds us all*
> *Of our pledge!*

Now the ring settled uncomfortably in Ryd's boot.

It was months before the caravan closed on Saldae and there through the escarpment they came upon a green landscape and the magic blue of the Mediterranean Sea. A giant rock outcrop sustained a hawk's view down onto the port and here the Roman traders could take on supplies and be guarded on the final step of their journey to their capital city. Rome the old capital, a centre of learning, trading and religion, now eclipsed by Constantinople and the Byzantines but still influenced at the tail of the eighth century by a Roman pope and a Christian church. And here was Ryd, arriving with a ring that guarded a pledge, but what pledge? Only Cai held the key and he was dead!

Saldae – Vespasian's Candle

'How do inhabitants of Saldae gain protection from the desert and the high Atlas?' asked Ryd.

Silas, gazing like a hawk down onto the town from the heights, replied, 'You can only enter the town on agreed market days. You have to stay outside the town's walls until the market day commences.'

'And from the sea?' ventured Ryd.

'Saldae is ruled from its rock; whoever controls the rock – the monkey peak – can signal to announce friend or foe. Beyond the escarpment there is another peak called "the sleeping woman"; whoever controls that peak rules the entire region! You could spend time running to the port each time a ship was seen on the horizon, but with large numbers to defend the port, there is no need to rush for weapons at the first sight of a ship. They build ships here. That is the key; ship workers are employed here in great numbers. Of course if a large fleet was seen approaching, a signal would be made from the monkey peak and all the workers would then move to arm. But there is another factor; they have been attacked here from the sea many times – Vandals, Byzantines. The citizens allow the trading power to fight the battles while they flee through the escarpment and disappear into the Atlas until their representatives negotiate a safe return.'

'So there is a port power and a Berber desert power,' deduced Ryd.

'The port power will never reform the desert power,' Silas reminded him. 'Islam dominates the desert power, and no matter how many Christians come to Saldae they will never reform Islam! The desert has its ways and its animals. Look at our camel; that beast rules our desert space.'

How different to Winswood, thought Ryd, where everyone was required to respond to every port arrival. Now if they increased their shipbuilding capacity they could solve their signalling dilemma. Here at Saldae the agricultural population hardly reacted to the rivalry between opposing sea powers. Power remained deep in the desert behind the escarpment, beyond the 'sleeping woman'. For Winswood, the religious dilemma remained pivotal; which religion would rule behind the Cornish escarpment? They had no camels at Winswood, camels that spat in your face, camels that could crush a rival's head, camels that urinated and sprayed backwards. A different beast controlled the Winswood space.

'And what of the ownership of land and trading rights?' asked Ryd.

'What is ownership? I have no use for the ownership of land. Look here at Saldae, once owned by the Romans, named by Vespasian after their Thracian horse rider god, stolen by the Vandals, overrun by the Byzantines – who owns Saldae? Saldae lives from its trade, its proximity to the safety of Rome, yet its position makes it a target. Saldae is owned by its mountains; the mountain and the desert determine whether Saldae lives or dies!'

'So where do you keep all your money and possessions, Silas? You don't believe in ownership, land ownership; how then do you retain a store of wealth?'

'Ah, wealth, you mean like the pharaohs of Egypt – you don't know about them, Ryd. Far, far to the east near our Holy Land there is a great river, the greatest river, and beside this river, hundreds of feet high, great pyramids of stone were built. Within these tombs – that's what they are, tombs for the great kings of Egypt – great treasure stores can be found. Of course once the workers bury the treasure they too can steal the treasure. And unless the workers at the tomb are killed the tombs will be robbed. But in answer to your question I would need to hold my possessions in some place free from the gaze of my slaves and my managers; my slaves are my weakness in this story, since my managers are family. So I have no option other than to share my wealth, share my wealth out amongst those people whom I trust. Can I trust you, Ryd?'

Before Ryd had answered, Silas continued, 'Where can you find friends, friends you can trust? A mountain kingdom, or an island kingdom? Political certainty and longevity is required, then supposing the ruling dynasty can withstand attack perhaps I will have a chance of recovering my assets. Or perhaps I should exchange my wealth for precious metal and conceal it in a cave high up in the Atlas! No, I need to keep a good portion of my wealth in what I can view and with my managers who operate on my behalf at the various trading points where my caravan stops. Also I will need to ensure I have credit with the old trading families who are known to me, and finally I will always seek to benefit my friends and contractual allegiances. Then if I suffer a great loss I will still have some capital upon which I can transfer my trading skill to survive. In these desert regions have you ever felt the ground quake?'

Ryd replied that he had never experienced the tremor that Silas described.

'In our region,' continued Silas, 'forces live deep in the earth that can destroy an entire city. Why, just a few days' sailing from Saldae you will find what we call volcanoes, and in the shadow of these monsters that spit molten rock into the sky all men quiver with fear. What use could I make of news informing me that Saldae was burnt to the ground and all my warehouses and possessions destroyed? I cannot be recompensed. What if foreign forces land and steal my goods? I'm left with nothing. There is an alternative. It results if I share my investments with those in political power. Then in my trading ring when I am damaged they are damaged, and they will support measures to return trade to normality as quickly as possible. I don't have a cave in the mountains filled with treasure; do you, Ryd?'

'We have a castle, and we might not have your pyramid but I assure you we hold a great treasure,' exclaimed Ryd.

'I have this caravan and further caravans dispersed through the desert. How do you make your treasure work? Surely it is a great expense to maintain its defence,' deduced Silas.

'The treasure isn't worked; it's defended by our castle and our corridor of death!'

'Your corridor of death is an expense and unless you grow your treasure, the expense of holding it secure yet inactive will eventually deplete your resources. You need to be involved in activities promoting your skills, your transaction skills, or someone will come and remove your treasure and your state will cease to function,' observed Silas. 'Sixty days south of Sijilmasa past the trading walls of Awdaghust lies a city full of gold and treasure enough for 10,000 camels, more; I've seen it!'

'You have seen the ten golden horses?' Ryd asked, remembering the tale.

'Now there is a treasure, a kingdom of gold, but it will disappear, it will be robbed,' said Silas. 'But to find the city you need a map just like the map on the back of my black slave girl!'

Ryd was startled to learn that Silas had a black female slave somewhere on the caravan with a map to the city of gold. Could that slave be the same slave he had seen?

'I prefer a kingdom that holds knowledge,' Silas continued, turning and walking on.

Ryd reflected upon the desert Jew's thoughts; would Winswood end like a broken pyramid? A looted pyramid? The Saxons barred the east. To the west lay the sea. The inability to increase trade led to internal pressures and discontent, and the sharing of resources was no longer fair – the Duchess had stirred the mixture and now nobody was safe, not even Ryd!

What force could Ryd bring to ensure the castle's survival?

Knowledge, Silas had said.

'Knowledge?' mumbled Ryd, but where was the black slave with the map?

Saldae was full of knowledge – Roman water courses, Arabic mathematics and Greek fire; now the latter was indeed of interest to anyone considering an improvement upon the corridor of death!

And then there was the ring and its special directional force.

With Silas gone, Ryd slid back into his cage and the caravan descended the escarpment out onto the coastal plain of Saldae. The most important point Ryd had learnt was that through building ships at the Duke's port an improvement in safety would result. Winswood's port area needed to be large enough to accommodate new industries and workers and this was where Winswood suffered serious limitations; the terrain at Winswood was ill suited. Alternative towns had port aspects more suitable for development with substantial rivers that could float in the materials required. The only alternative was to prohibit arrivals at the Duke's port and insist goods be unloaded elsewhere, then the castle would be able to function as a security castle, not a merchant or trading castle. In fact it would exist wholly as a treasure castle and therefore any number of ships arriving off the port would automatically count as foes! And if it could not be a treasure castle, well, why not a slave castle? Ryd had rejected the idea of a knowledge castle.

Silas lost no time in attending the old Roman meeting rooms. Although the city had been occupied by Vandals and Byzantines the traders still sought to maintain the structure and organisation of the earlier Roman period. Many important trading families had disappeared, but merchant profits were so large these families had been replaced. Silas concluded his sale of Ryd satisfactorily.

'So, Ryd, I have concluded your sale to the Roman gold fleet. I have received a fair sum, a good return on my investment, and now I beg you to attend at the bathhouse where your new masters wish to make your acquaintance and engage your services. You can choose three slaves to take with you for which you will owe me. You won't find any facial markings on these slaves and they all have clear backs. In Mecca they mark all children on the face forty days after birth, three scars on this side and then three on the other side of the face. They don't wish their children to be kidnapped; it tells you the origin of the child. All markings have a meaning; some think it keeps them free, but just remember that slave with the river marked to the horse city of gold – she isn't free!'

Ryd nodded; how would he ever forget that slave and her map to the horse city of gold? Some markings might keep you free but some markings attract you and you stay attracted right through your life.

*

Silas had been attracted to the name Tamar and he invited Ryd to accompany 'Tamar', one of his slaves, on her daily outing to the market. Until this meeting Ryd had no idea why Silas had desired the name; why had he chosen a link to a far-away isle?

She had the bluest of eyes and her hair that peeked out of her scarf was blonde. How could she have come from these parts? They were unable to converse. She could only speak the local language of the market, yet as they moved from one stall to another they communicated with their eyes, smiles and gestures. Tamar, Silas's slave.

Silas had sent her to the market for honey and a pancake called bourjeje. Silas's wife had a larger request and the young Tamar embarked upon fulfilling her mistress's wishes first. Moving to the east she purchased what Ryd heard was za'faran. This was a golden yellow additive that the mistress used in her bath water; she called it her gold and it was the most expensive purchase at the market place. From the southern stalls Tamar purchased oranges. Turning west she bought red chillies and finally north, towards the port, she purchased some green peppers and olives. At the market's centre she found the honey and the pancake, the bourjeje. The honey would have been the only taste that Ryd knew from Winswood.

The port stalls and their fresh fish beckoned at the quay and in the final purchase, young Tamar bought some octopus before crossing back to the centre of the market and the orange stall on the walk home. Smiling at the stall holder Ryd noticed a silence; the birds had stopped singing; the market folk looked at each other curiously and then came a violent tremor. A shuddering shaking moment. The ground beneath their feet shook violently, everyone stood as if glued to the ground, fear on every face, the tremor continued, the shaking and now a noise, a beat, a clattering beat brought the stalls to the ground. Fruit rolled across the floor, people sought to steady themselves, Tamar grabbed the fallen orange stall and gripping the wood she started to wail. 'Ahh … ahhhhh …'

'Calm stay calm *stay* calm,' said Ryd, his voice rising as his fear rose.

People were rushing from every building. Ryd thought a monster was about to emerge from the side of one building adjacent to the market. The shaking had become so violent it appeared that a monster's body would burst through the wall from inside. Suddenly the roof collapsed; first one half then the other sheared off and the whole market arena was covered with a red dust. It was impossible to see another person even separated from them by just a few yards. Ryd covered his face and mouth from the descending dust; he had no idea which way to look. There were shrieks. Ryd had stopped crying out; he knew he had to wait until the tremor ceased and the dust settled.

Then just as abruptly as the tremors had started they ceased. The quake had lasted no longer than thirty seconds yet several buildings had collapsed, fruit was rolling around the market and everyone was agitated and scared. Would there be an aftershock, a repeat? It was too late to consider that possibility since screams were coming from people near the collapsed building and everyone was wondering what to do. Should they risk searching the rubble or wait, wait until all likelihood of a further tremor had disappeared?

Ryd crossed to Tamar and held her, giving her encouragement. As he looked into her eyes her beauty appealed. Ryd clutched her close as she brushed the dust from her face and hands. She was still trembling; he was enjoying this moment enveloping her body, taking in all her smells. He gazed into her eyes – in this moment he found love.

'Just a small tremor, so this is what Silas means by a quake,' said Ryd. But before he was safe a horrendous crash was heard and another of the buildings close to the market collapsed in a shower of dust.

By the time the shopping tour had ended and the quake ceased, Silas had caught Ryd just like an octopus. Gold would lure him back to the African continent, but it was the flower of gold – the 'za'faran' – that Ryd wanted from Saldae. Perhaps he could rescue Tamar and return with her to Britain's green isle, if Silas released him from his basket trap.

Ryd attended one final meeting with Silas, but he kept secret his interest in Silas's golden flower.

'I am delighted that you survived the shipwreck and our quake,' said Silas. 'I can trust you, Ryd; your gold convoy colleagues will pass through Saldae on their return to Carmarthen and you will join them. I am pleased to have assisted you on your journey. Oh, you can keep the ring,' Silas added, smiling. 'I have no need of it – what Jew has need of a cross?'

Ryd shifted nervously, the ring swiftly forgotten; he was looking at Silas's animal cages.

'What did you see?' asked Silas.

'A beast,' said Ryd. 'I would like to return with the hyena.'

'But Ryd, you have seen your first elephant here in Saldae; why not the elephant?' Silas laughed, shaking his head; why did Ryd wish to return with an animal, especially the hyena?

Ryd had seen an elephant, a massive elephant with huge tusks, but he had no wish to jeopardise his chances of returning safely; an elephant with its massive ears hearing everything was not perhaps appropriate for Winswood. 'The hyena,' he repeated.

'Of course, of course I will ensure that it is caged in the port in readiness for your departure. The hyena, why the hyena?'

'The hyena is my choice, it must be the hyena.'

'And you shall have the hyena, Ryd – a gift, and what will you return to trade with me?'

'Treasure,' said Ryd, 'one day I will come for treasure and return with treasure! You find me Greek fire and I will bring you treasure.'

Silas shook his head; some things even a Jew could not source. But slaves he could source, and it was agreed for Ryd to view Silas's female slaves.

Gul was her name, young, long brown hair, and a dancer. Ryd sat formally. She asked if he would like to see her dance. He nodded. She began gently – so who would play snake, buyer or slave? Her dance was hypnotic, she moved easily across the carpet, an exotic odalisque used to pleasing men, yielding. In Ryd she awoke the beast. Later in his dreams he would touch and glide across her golden body, his fingers checking her unblemished back, yet he always turned, beckoned by Tamar, the face of a beautiful blonde, and always woke in a sweat fearing the map on the black slave had gone. Later he arranged for Gul and two companions, all owned by Silas, to accompany him on his voyage. Silas had chosen to invest in Ryd. 'You'll be paid,' said Ryd, 'with the return of the convoy, with the return of the swallow, I will return with gold.' His love for Tamar remained his secret.

Ryd had to wait a week before the galley bound for Carmarthen was sighted. He found out everything he could about the Byzantines' 'Greek fire'. The galley crew were surprised to find he had survived the storms and even more surprised to load his hyena and his slaves, but that job was accomplished and after climbing the monkey peak for one last time Ryd was ready to depart Saldae. At the monkey peak he stumbled on a Roman coin: Vespasian on one side and Fortuna on the other. What had Vespasian seen from up here, a ring or a beast? What would be Ryd's fortune after this last view from the monkey peak? What would he do next? What had Cihtric said when viewing Lundy Island? 'It's not what you see, it's what you do!'

Ryd had learned to be cautious in the showing of signs; the wrong sign can kill. He worried whether a curse lay on the ring that nestled beneath his tunic. How do you remove a curse from a ring? And Greek fire – he had observed at the shipyard the special siphons used to deliver torrents of fire; it was indeed valuable technology but technology that the Byzantine owners were unwilling to share. Furthermore the mixture to ignite the weapon and fire the dragon was in short supply and unavailable for Ryd's corridor of death. How could he gain control of such a dark force? Some secrets could never be shared and his mind turned to a woman's back: not the one with the lustre of a golden jewel or the one emerging from a saffron bath, but the ebony back scarred with a map, a map to the horse city of gold.

Rome Galley to Carmarthen

Utarba was the black captain of the Roman galley returning from Rome to Carmarthen; Ryd knew Utarba from the outbound voyage nine months earlier bringing Welsh and Irish gold to Rome. Utarba's vessel made good progress from Saldae through the straits of Gibraltar. The cargo included a black female slave. This slave Ryd had seen on the slave route to Sijilmasa. But was it the slave with the map? If only he could view her back.

Passing Cape Trafalgar they followed the coast northwards without mishap until they turned into the Bay of Biscay to touch the northern Spanish coast and link with another Roman gold route. Everyone spoke of gold. The seas and sky were dark and bellicose.

At last Ryd was able to question Utarba.

'The crew seem pensive; do you have any news for me?' Ryd asked.

'Rome is in turmoil,' replied Utarba. 'Some of the aristocrats opposing Pope Leo made an attempt upon his life. Only the Frisian nobles of King Karl enabled Leo to escape; some say the Pope sought shelter with the King in the north. We fear should he return to Rome. There will be war; each man is concerned for his family and the choices they will make.'

Ryd decided to avoid the theme of Rome and to question Utarba on Greek fire; it was time to share some knowledge, perhaps divulge a secret. 'If there is war what are the navies doing about Greek fire?' he asked.

'What do you know on that subject?' enquired Utarba.

'I watched the commissioning in Saldae of a siphon system; it's a terrifying weapon. Who holds the secrets?'

'The Byzantines,' answered Utarba. 'We have dismantled captured weapons, but never managed to break the secret of the material composition that causes the liquid to combust. The siphon and its system of delivery we were able to reproduce but all that is worthless without the secret ingredient. Look, see these goods we bring to Wales – pottery, tools, silks, even wine, there is a secret behind each of these manufactures. Only our marble ballast has nothing to hide. I cannot help you with Greek fire, Ryd.' 'Then what can you tell me about your new slave?' continued Ryd.

'A small present from the merchant you call Silas,' responded Utarba. 'He charged me with finding more about her – I have been unable to get a word from her. We share an odd connection. My Roman foster father found me after a naval campaign off the shores of Egypt. I was unable to communicate with him on either my tribe or my home; this girl suffers from the same problem. The only difference between her and myself is that she has the strangest of maps scarred on her back.'

Ryd had known it; this was indeed the same slave girl he had journeyed with to the slave auction at Sijilmasa.

'What sort of secret do you think is traced in the scar lines?' asked Ryd.

'Well, the ochre horse suggests a city, the gold city perhaps.'

'Ah, gold,' whispered Ryd.

'Gold,' said Utarba, nodding.

There was something uncomfortable about the use of the word and yet something inordinately exciting. 'Gold!' They both called out in unison and laughed.

Utarba's lips offered nothing further on the gold subject, so Ryd referenced the yellow metal to the Pope's predicament in

Rome. 'Would you be guilty of treason if you delivered the Welsh gold back to Rome, to a Rome ruled by the Pope's enemies?' he asked.

Utarba nodded. 'At sea as a captain I make life and death decisions. No one can help me at sea and those who disagree with my decisions only have a watery option,' he pronounced, pointing to the turbulent waters of the bay. 'Who did you pray to when you were shipwrecked in the water, Ryd? Neptune, Poseidon, tell me; it surely wasn't God, was it?'

Ryd sympathetically shook his head.

'When these decisions are made, Ryd, you turn to a protector – I might choose Egypt's St Anthony or another saint. In the water most men call on their gods. On land the pope with the largest army will suffice. We now have a war, Ryd; war is the father and king of all things. Are you familiar with the Greek Heraclitus?'

Ryd nodded. 'But for a long protracted war you need gold,' he said, 'you need treasure!'

'I thought your chief concern was justice,' said Utarba. 'When we met last summer justice was your main theme; now after your African experiences you have turned towards gold. Well, remember, with gold you can always demand a winner's justice.'

'You are right,' said Ryd. 'The Duchess represents the winner's, nay, the ruler's justice; I was wrong to focus upon such matters. I learnt much from Silas. He spends no time worrying about justice. For the Jew there is no appeal court and even if there were the process could last for years and there would be no profit. The fear man feels when on the wrong side of the winner's justice has a long timeline: weeks, months, years; why, natural disasters like quakes seem such short time frames in comparison. So now I seek gold!'

Utarba knew all about the power of gold and Rome's campaign to safeguard the politically sensitive trade routes to the yellow metal. 'Gold,' he said, nodding.

The Bay of Biscay proved a terrifying experience; slave and sailor alike suffered as the weather worsened and the seas proved ever more treacherous. The galley was lucky to survive the voyage around the Bay before cutting between the Ile d'Ouessant and the French mainland on a northerly course to arrive opposite the British coast. Ryd's three slaves watched anxiously as the coast of Britain appeared.

'This is the land where the Phoenicians came to trade tin,' said Ryd. 'Close on this coast is an island where twice a day the sea covers a causeway. On this island the traders come to buy tin.'

'This must be the island that Tamar spoke about,' said Gul. 'Tamar's mother spoke of such an island near their home. She spoke of God's ring thrown into a cove, a cove with a giant stone ring.'

Ryd was surprised by this remark. He had hoped to gain information on Tamar from his slaves, and here within sight of his beloved country the girls at last spilled information giving good reason for Silas to name a slave Tamar. This may well have been the country of her birth. But where was the cove with God's ring? Despite combing of the coastline for clues the whereabouts of the cove remained secret, shrouded in the coastline mist.

The galley slowly made its way west to pass the great estuary of the Tamar, making for the dangerous waters of Land's End before coiling up the Cornish toe towards Lundy. Here the galley entered the realm of the dragon. To the east the great dragon castle at Castle Winswood, north Cornwall. This land had always been feared, feared for its people, its justice, its corridor of death and the treacherous seas that disguised dragons' teeth. Further north, just thirty miles away, another dragon snorted at vessels from the Gower peninsula in Wales. Utarba's Roman galley sighted this Welsh signpost before following the Welsh coast westwards to the mouth of the River Towy and the entrance to Carmarthen, or Moridunum as it is called by the Romans. In Carmarthen the galley would load Welsh gold and any passengers bound for Rome.

On this final leg of the voyage to Carmarthen Ryd didn't have a chance to question Utarba. Ryd's interests centred on navigational aids and he pressed the Roman navigation master about the properties of iron and the method to obtain direction from a Norse lodestone. Ingvar had told him that his iron ring would have the same properties as a lodestone, an ability to always point to the north. No matter what obstacle you confronted, the ring or the lodestone would always point in the correct direction. That was an advantage. If only life could be similar, if only there were some device that could bring the owner always back onto the right path. What was the correct track? Ryd wondered how he could reserve his place at the table for making correct decisions. Would the ring point him in the right direction?

The Christians could offer Ryd a lodestone. The Christians assured believers their lodestone was the only secure path to God and his kingdom. The pagans could choose help from a variety of gods and goddesses. It wasn't surprising that a conflict developed. At first feudal obligations and ties stood above these conflicts. Then supporters of the different faiths obtained land and political power. At last they could play a role in the feudal equation, dine at the feudal high table. So for how long could pagans and their own secret groups dismiss this single Christian political threat?

There were monarchs like Karl who chose Christianity as a shaping influence that could be managed to support political aims. Pagans had every reason to fear this king. Yet Karl's support for the Christian church was not common among every monarch and chieftain in Europe. Paganism held in Cornwall in the eighth century; Christianity struggled to win support. In Rome the theme of importance lay in ownership: which aristocratic bloodline held the office of pope, which Roman family could stay advantaged by owning the office of pope?

Lower in the feudal rankings, Ryd's concern lay in avoiding bad luck. He feared his lack of strong religious convictions lessened his importance at clan meetings. Furthermore he was troubled with the ring still hidden in the hyena's cage, the ring of certain death. He had no reason to embrace Christianity: his experiences supported reasons not to convert; after all, his pagan beliefs had saved him during the shipwreck. Pagan beliefs demanded sacrifice. To ensure continued good fortune he would need to affirm his pagan beliefs and make a sacrifice.

Utarba, the feared black captain, had already cast the die; he would sacrifice the need to return to Rome. These thoughts were not passed to the Carmarthen loyalists about to load gold onto the Roman galley. Utarba had chosen to steal the Pope's gold. The royal passenger on the galley returning to Rome would necessitate Utarba's asking a favour of Ryd. On the return voyage to Rome a young Irish princess called Morwenna had been assured passage on the vessel. She had undertaken to take holy orders in Rome.

Of course Utarba's position had no relevance for Ryd. Why should Ryd be concerned with the Welsh gold? Ryd would be returning to Winswood. But could he return without being condemned for playing a role in the disappearance of the gold, the girl and the galley? And where was the black slave?

Utarba had kept his new slave away from everyone's view until one afternoon in Carmarthen the black slave was escorted to the baths and failed to return. Utarba flew into a fury and despatched members of the crew to find the girl. Ryd used this chance to join the men and search this seaport at the mouth of the River Towy.

Ryd's search centred on the bathhouse; he concluded that the girl had attracted attention and been abducted. Ryd was well known in Carmarthen where in the past he had arranged the transportation of holy blue stones to Kilkhampton, stones that were needed for every warrior's grave. He made his way through the lodging quarters until he was halted by a dreadful scream. With two of the crew in attendance he entered a dwelling to find the black slave being forced down upon a table. Held down by several swarthy Welshmen, the girl was being sliced across the back with a huge blade. It seemed that these folk were set upon removing a portion of skin from the girl's back. They were removing the map!

Ryd let out a cry of anger and flailing with his sword rushed among the slave's abductors. Blood spurted from the girl's back wound; the men had no intention of giving her up. A ferocious fight took place with one man losing part of his arm and another receiving a slice wound through the thigh. The Welsh retreated and Ryd and his colleagues withdrew with their female slave, saving her from the cutting table.

At last Ryd could view her back for himself. It was the map. The same map he had seen when Ingvar had run his finger along the lines; here was the horse in yellow ochre. They had saved the girl's life but now they had to patch her wounds and return her to Utarba!

Ryd, Hero of Lundy and Castle Winswood

Utarba had cast off the lines from the gold galley and the gold convoy had once more started for Rome. Within hours they lay in the lee of Lundy; the Viking escort ships then nosed eastwards, ready to turn to the south to follow the Cornish coast off Kilkhampton and Winswood towards Land's End. With the Irish princess Morwenna aboard, instead of immediately raising its sail and pursuing the escorts, the great galley slowed in the water while the oarsmen made for the Duke's port at Kylgh. Abruptly within sight of the beach Utarba signalled his crew and pointed to Ryd's raft holding the hyena cage. They drew closer to the entrance to Ryd's home port, and a rowing vessel and the raft were expertly lowered into the water. The princess was viewing the unloading process with interest when suddenly she and her retainers were seized by Utarba's guards, bound and taken to the side where Ryd's rowing vessel had been made fast.

It was Ryd who had picked up on the negative disposition of the galley crew. He had already come to the conclusion that a return to Rome lay in doubt. That left the crew with one other dilemma: what to do with Morwenna? Ryd had no wish to learn that the young girl had been cast overboard. He had tackled Utarba with his suspicions and gained firm agreement with the captain that Morwenna would be passed into his custody. In the seas off Lundy, Utarba could choose to honour his agreement with Ryd or sail on.

'Your journey ends here, Morwenna,' Utarba shouted. 'We have changed plans; you will accompany Ryd to Winswood. Do not be distressed, we have our orders, Ryd will look after you. Rome is at war and the Pope has been removed. No harm will come to you with the Cornish.' And with that, the princess was lowered amongst the rowers. Unbeknown to the young princess, Ryd the unsung Cornish hero had saved her life. Her retainers looked on in terror; within hours they would all be cast into the sea.

Utarba stood tall on the galley with the black slave girl standing next to him and now he beckoned Ryd.

'A surprise for you, Ryd! This galley takes the last Welsh gold, there will be no more. You will need a map to an endless supply of the yellow metal.' Then pointing at his black slave Utarba commanded, 'Take this girl, care for her map. Take the girl, I have enough gold!' And with that order Utarba pushed the black slave towards Ryd. 'Her name is Kambon paga,' he added.

Ryd was shocked but wasted little time in considering Utarba's decision. Ryd took hold of his slave, who showed no sign of dissent, and arranged her and his other slaves and possessions on the small rowing vessel and the raft that would beach them below Castle Winswood. He wondered whether Silas had ordered the girl to be given to him, thus ensuring his return to the Dark Continent.

Ryd paid little attention to Morwenna; his concern was his raft and the caged hyena which floated beautifully away from the galley. Ryd sat next to his black slave Kambon paga; he waved back to Utarba awkwardly. He wanted to come ashore quickly whilst ideal beaching conditions prevailed. Home at last, thought Ryd; how long had it been – nine months? But how was he to explain to the clan Morwenna's plight?

Ryd was unaware that the Irish were no longer feudal superiors of the Cornish or that the Duke on seeing Morwenna would insist on a ransom. The Duke made the laws; no other judges appeared at the Duke's circle, certainly none of the nine that Ryd had seen in his African vision. The circle existed but King Arthur's laws were as distant from the Duke as Dozmary Pool lay from Kylgh. The sword Excalibur had been discarded in that pool; the great sword forged long ago by the giants on Lundy was now lost and had no influence at the dragon castle. A truly dark age dominated and the castle's duchess had already raised an accusative finger at Ryd, so how long could Ryd avoid her wrath?

In his discussion with Utarba in Carmarthen, Ryd had made his choice. Morwenna must be taken from the galley. Ryd knew the galley would not reach Rome. Icosium, Saldae, he could not be sure where his former colleagues would navigate the galley but it certainly was not going to Rome.

Morwenna sobbed; Ryd's slave girls could not console her. 'My father will see you destroyed,' she hissed.

'Calm yourself, Princess, or you will disturb the beast,' replied Ryd. 'See how the hyena views you; quieten yourself. Your destination is now Castle Winswood and you must gain composure or you will meet with the rush!' and he made a chopping movement towards his own neck. The great dragon castle now waited to entertain a princess and the princess waited to meet the Cornish dragon.

Since no large vessel had entered the Duke's port, no signal had been raised for the castle folk to attend on the little band that reached the beach – Ryd's raft and the small craft carrying Morwenna and the slaves. The Duke's workers at the port watching the arrival left their tasks and surrounded Ryd, who was immediately recognised.

Ryd's possessions, slaves and beast and Morwenna were set on carts and the long haul to the castle was soon underway. Not until they reached the slave stockade did any appreciable number of men gather to observe the caged beast's progress up to the castle. Any movements east up the corridor of death needed permission and after some delay and deliberation to see that the way was clear with no inter-ruptions, the carts pulled into the corridor and the long mile was negotiated until the treasure hill and the great castle came into view.

Morwenna gasped; so this was the horror castle and in front the ancient treasure hill that stored a colossal treasure hoard. The carts moved further up the Coombe valley until they had passed the treasure hill and entered the Kylgh stronghold. Here Morwenna was entrusted to a captain of guards and removed under escort to the castle. The beast and the slaves moved down along a track and into the treasure hill. With the female slaves released into the bathhouse, the beast's cage was set at the entrance to the treasure labyrinth and Ryd with several guards entered the lower vault.

It wasn't long before Ryd reached a stall held for one of the Duchess's sacred blue stallions. He wasn't sure where to set the beast until out of the bathhouse corridor appeared the Duchess with her dwarf Lucco carrying a flaming torch.

'Ryd … at last … you thought you would escape my wrath!' The flaming red torch and the flickering shadows cast upon the vault walls evoked a horrifying picture. The Duchess was truly to be feared and Ryd, who had been gone from the castle for many months, stepped back to take a breath – he was still in great danger, his father was nowhere to be seen. How could Ryd divert the Duchess?

'Duchess Gisela, did you see the slaves I brought, and out there a beast?' Ryd asked, pointing.

'What beast?' she replied.

'An African beast; this will quicken tongues when prisoners

enter our torture chamber. Come, let me show you,' and with that Ryd walked with the Duchess back to the cage.

'We're not finished – you challenged me,' she darted at Ryd.

'I challenged your interpretation,' he replied. 'Your horse whispered that my wagon driver had secret associations and endangered Winswood; I … er.'

'Your views put no meat on the bones in this lair,' spat the Duchess.

'Ah, but let me show you some meat now,' countered Ryd, and they both turned a corner to confront the caged beast.

'A … wha … what is this?' the Duchess gasped. The striped hyena glared at the Duchess and Lucco hid behind her.

'Do you think the Duke will like this beast? Which cell should I allocate the animal?' Ryd asked.

The Duchess took some time to observe the beast before answering; she was impressed. 'Take it to the central chamber – yes, use that part of the labyrinth so we can all see the beast,' the Duchess replied. 'For torture you say …' And she grabbed his arm. 'Did you see its teeth, huh? Teeth or the cliff, Ryd? We are not finished … and what else? I hear there is a girl,' the Duchess added. Who had whispered this information, her hawk?

'Morwenna – an Irish princess bound for Rome,' replied Ryd.

'Irish – we have refused to pay them tribute – but that's the Duke's problem. We will meet later. You brought slaves too … this will earn you time; what else do you have that may spare your life?'

'Greek fire,' replied Ryd, 'I have knowledge of Greek fire. Such a weapon in the hands of our men will make the corridor of death a truly fiery spectacle – a journey to the dragon's lair – such fire you have never observed in your life!'

'Well, we will hear later when you address the clan. Knowledge ... huh, the Duke would prefer gold,' said the Duchess defiantly and she sped away, Lucco at her heels.

Ryd breathed a sigh of relief; he had survived their first encounter. As long as the Duke supported him the Duchess would temper her pursuit. Besides, Ryd no longer sought to tangle with the Duchess over justice; he sought gold, a winner's gold to purchase the beautiful flower of za'faran from Vespasian's city, honouring a master of horse. On the monkey peak Vespasian had seen a ring; in Rome he would build the Colosseum. Ryd had seen the beast and he had returned to Winswood determined to exercise its authority.

Part 2

Riddle of the Oak

*In his dream he had viewed
the back of a Saxon woman.*

A Mystic's View of the Future and a Reminder of the Past

Through the summer of 798 AD and beyond, Ryd had been absent from Castle Winswood, missing important events in the pagan calendar. One clan custom that took place in 799 AD involved selecting, on a frosty January morning, a blade of ice from a woodland pool. This blade of ice was read by the clan reader seeking to probe into the future; his interpretation defined the risks and opportunities facing the clan and helped them develop a strategy to secure the clan's regional advantage. The reporting of this strange winter custom follows:

An icy mist rose across a shallow forest pool; a warrior broke ice and picking up a blade passed it to a dark-robed figure, a reader, a mystic. The small gathering included Cihtric, his son Gavin and their supporters. Cihtric called the gathering to attention in the absence of the Duke:

'We meet this day, a Friday, to read the signs and plan our year. This icy blade is chosen; we ask the Circle's spirits to spill our troubles and guide us.'

(The blade of ice contained a strange motif – a shape like a letter N and next an antler shape containing a trapped bubble. The robed Reader fastened upon the blade in his hand.)

The Reader began:

'A thousand bubbles rise and chance life within our spray.
Each bubble conveys a secret
And as secrets fashion
From the multitude

We can choose just one –
So who will lead us?
Who will be tasked?

Choose!

Once chosen
The bubble descends, down to where all secrets and sorcery mingle
Till
Expectant it rises again and returns
Bearing a burden
Sharing a secret.

Here
Coated in winter's frost
Frozen within this pane
Are all the coming year's forces – trapped.
Now spill the secret and confirm our luck.'

(The Reader gazed for some moments intently at the ice and pointed.)

'Observe our weaknesses – we break to the east, here the Saxon
    power.
To the North and Wales we link – are we allies still?
To the west the sea, always a danger.
Now trace this single line – a message, a tribute?
Will it feed us
Or clamour to be fed?
And here – this single line of contact intends no balance.'

'So we need a sea power, an alliance to come from the west?'
interjected Cihtric.

'For our shape someone must travel and find support to oppose the Saxon threat to the east,' replied the mystic Reader.

'And the bubble?' asked Cihtric.

'Ah, you speak of the secret. A foreigner will come to Winswood, within our circle, to learn – mark this well, the body cannot be trusted, Winswood will court a great danger! The person's tongue must be loosened before Winswood can be safe,' continued the mystic.

'We trade, we have many foreigners in Kylgh; how shall we find this traitor?' questioned Gavin.

'I speak not of traitors; I speak more of a force that will act against Winswood. This is a foreigner. This foreigner will come to Winswood with a secret of great danger to these walls. More I cannot say. Consult your hawks, your horses. Beware the foreigner, he cannot be trusted; he will seek to serve you but Winswood will not be served,' emphasised the mystic.

'Perhaps we should light upon our own miscreants first; like moths they will be tempted to the candle. Better we control our own traitorous aspect than have it scattered as seed all around us,' Cihtric observed.

'The journey line,' queried Gavin, 'can you read from their shields, their flags, ship's prow, any signs to attribute a nation or tribe?'

'Viking! All Viking,' the mystic responded.

'Ryd, my eldest, sails with the Viking and we await his return! Oh may that day be near. But we cannot wait for his arrival; we should choose now who will travel to make the tie,' concluded Cihtric. 'To maintain our shape and achieve balance from the west a venture must be undertaken soon.'

'And luck?' asked Gavin.

'I see no luck, I feel no luck, yet knowledge of these signs will prepare us well. With action rests success. For good fortune sacrifice and trust in our circle's history and its legends,' concluded the mystic.

'So a loss, a journey, there will be pain and suffering before rebirth,' mocked Gavin.

'Don't mock. What has been lost?' queried Cihtric.

'Why, our safety, our security – I will undertake the journey, Father; there, what are your orders?' Gavin responded.

'First let's see what your brother and the Vikings bring, then we will decide if we renew our tribute with the Irish or move upon an alliance with another power to balance and oppose the Saxons.'

'And the bubble, Father?' pressed Gavin. 'To me it's more like a RING.'

'With the warming of the weather every tongue will loosen – I'll confer with our robed Reader,' said Cihtric.

Then moving to disperse, Gavin whispered quietly to his father, 'I will change this if I become a counsellor.'

'And why?'

'Pah … these are all ideas dug from the Reader's soul; why, he plucks … bubbles, secrets, he is as mad as the dwarf Lucco – we need to evaluate each problem to the north, south, east and west,' Gavin argued. 'I see a ring!'

Cihtric countered, 'Our method delves under the covers, under the leaves, deeper. Your elder brother is more sympathetic to our approach, yet I do not deny that there are other methods that could weigh our situation. So long as action is taken!'

It was May that year of 799 AD before Ryd returned and after a brief clan reunion his brother Gavin made ready to depart for Verden, to seek out the court of Karl the Great and seal an alliance with the Franks.

At daybreak on the morning of Gavin's departure, Cihtric and Ryd lay asleep in the castle. Grooms had been busy, Lucco had saddled the Duchess's stallion and she had left for a meeting with an escort. Cutting out along a lonesome track through gorse to the left of the Clovelly road two riders waited on the Duchess, one blond riding with a hawk, the other jet black-haired and armed with a fearsome battle axe. Both were clad in what looked like bear skin covering their shoulders. Before the sun could poke up beyond the yellow gorse the two riders acknowledged the arrival of the Duchess. She had travelled north on the same track as the great circle race, but instead of pursuing the race loop as it turned south she had cut off and continued northwest heading towards the 'Henna cliff', the cliff of the ravens just four miles from Kylgh. The Duchess on her blue stallion and Lucco on another blue mount were accompanied by a further twenty mounted warriors all slowly making their way through the mist towards the cliffs. The riders were in no hurry, no conversation took place, their horses maintained a gentle rhythm, they had made this journey many times before.

Within the hour the cliff came into sight, where a beacon had been lit and about thirty armed men waited with a prisoner. This man was bound and forced to the ground at the approach of the Duchess. The riders drew up in a curve and a log well over ten feet in length was pulled from the fire onto the ground. The prisoner was drawn up to face the Duchess in front of the glowing log.

'Do you have anything to say,' the Duchess asked, 'before hawk and stallion consider your sentence?'

The prisoner made no effort to speak but he tried to draw himself up to his full height. The blond warrior dismounted and brought the hawk eyeball to eyeball with the prisoner's face. The hawk's eyes fixed upon the bearded prisoner. The prisoner closed his eyes.

'Do you have anything to say?' the Duchess repeated.

The prisoner remained tight-lipped, silent.

The Duchess looked across to her black-haired warrior who, clasping his battle axe, dismounted.

The Duchess's stallion was quiet.

'Did the hawk speak?' queried the Duchess. The blond shook his head. 'And the stallion?' The dark-haired warrior also shook his head.

'Then remove his head!' ordered the Duchess.

Before the prisoner could reconsider his silence, warriors seized him by the hair and forced his head under the burning log. The Duchess shouted again, 'Remove his head, if he won't use his tongue he has no need of it!' Several warriors were needed to secure the head below the burning log. The man screamed as the first axe blow fell; it missed his neck and sank into his cheek. The Duchess was angry. 'No words, no comments, then my hawk will have your lips, your tongue, your eyes.'

The head was now secure under the log and a second blow from the axe cut into the neck. A scream had exploded from the man's throat before a final blow removed his head. The severed head, eyes bulging and hair smoking, was kicked towards the hawk.

The Duchess's stallion made no sound.

'I have no need for hyenas,' the Duchess shouted, 'I have my sea and my dwarf.'

And with that exclamation the dwarf began an eerie count: 'A toad's beak, a pail's doubt, a pecan's boast, a slug's toe, a fool's doublet.' With a flourish the dwarf removed the doublet from the dead man and rummaged through the clothes looking for any other items of value. His search complete, the severed body was grabbed by two warriors and hurled over the cliff, falling almost 500 feet onto the rocks below. The incoming tide and the crabs would share anything the ravens left.

Later, once the hawk had vacated the skull, the dark-haired warrior retrieved the head; he placed it in a sack, smiled at Lucco and mounted for the return ride to the castle.

The Duchess's sentencing was complete; another body had been hurled over the cliff to meet the dragons' teeth. Where in her youth had the Duchess become so hardened to the act of beheading? Of course it must have been in Verden, the 'Reiterstadt' of her youth. Yet how had she hidden the trauma, the guilt of her survival, the guilt of the Saxon sharing? In 782 AD she wasn't in Verden at the massacre.

First came the deeds; the Duchess's presence on the cliff at many Cornish executions established the reputation of the Henna cliff and the dragon folk. Her words and the explanation for her fury could atrophy in the ingot of time unless they were recorded on that eventful day, and they were; she spoke surveying the scene of her justice:

Ah the rain, my fire still smoulders
So many sounds, so many memories to wash … away
My cloth will never dry; dark clouds have layered me with a
*   lifetime for complaining.*
The fire here will consume this fool's cloth and his shoe
The gods won't be wanting his complaint or his families
Sacrifice is only for those free of blemish.
This smoke entreats no action from the formulators of true wisdom
*   and justice.*

See
My ravens thrive
Whenever a body braces the floor
Sea tides roll and roar

It's a raven fest.
Crabs clatter and crawl dependent on Neptune's timely permission
Each anxious for a juicy bite,
Black feathers yield to raging white
Foam!

My hawk and horse merit great fame
Delivering verdicts in my name
Justice is my preserve –
Another guilty patriot, prepare to fling him –
But first, a burning, a cutting
Just like the Franks delivered on my brother.
He just nine and I only fourteen
As the Irminsul our holiest shrine was attacked, it was twenty-five
    years ago
We children hid high, climbing a tree, enduring the cries
The burning and raping began, the Franks learnt so much from
    Boniface at Fritzlar; fifty years earlier Thor's oak was burnt.
Frank riders now bent breath beneath our tree
Until my brother fell on them,
He ran to lure them away from me and Fastrada my older sister.
I found his headless body
His golden locks … a memory, his lovely head … lost
In some worming grave.
I touched his blood, wiped my cloth with it, wet and even now I
    weep,
The scars so deep, nothing, nothing will amend, nothing in this
    time.

Fastrada was sixteen, she disappeared,
After the smoke rings … nothing.
She was the same age as the stirrup king's first wife
Hildegard.
Just a few strands of hair remained tangled in the bough – I've
    kept them close.

Franks sold Saxon women to the Moors
Slavery
No fine rings
No cloth
That's why my father was happy to see me brought here away from
    the Franks.
We keep our heads here.
My dwarf notes each one in our gallery
Their faces stare
Guilt,
Honour is done.

Sometimes I travel further, a short ride
To the waterfall of tears
And there I cry, I cry for Fastrada
I remember her rings, her eyes, her fine voice

The oracle watches, silently observing me every time. 'Ring or
    beast, what did you see?' Ah ... what do I hear?
As if my journey could ever contain the beast that rages here in
    this breast!
For beast I work
For beast I claim this cliff
I'll tolerate no rivals
I need no hyena to scold,
I only hear the beast, the voices, the voices!
I cannot heal my own wounds.
How does the Duke expect me to heal others?

See
Down there the ravens urge each other – open the man's breast,
Let his soul slip away, his mystery leak to the sky!
Escape before the crabs embrace and turn with sucking urchins to
    dance with him
Down to the depths.

They seek advantage,
I leave advantage for the Duke and those that carry arms.
And for visions, I have nothing to do with visions; we have the
  Reader,
And that new religion.

Their priests commence with a small need for property and of
  course advantage before dabbling, dabbling in Justice. But they
  never applaud,
They only complain,
Like me they carry a wound; their Christ carried a wound and a
  cross.
Enough, time advances
I must relate my tale
To Duke and aide
In Bodmin my man will ride to crow
Another guilty party lies below!
But you ask
Where did I learn the language of hawk and horse?
In my birth land
Sometimes a shriek sometimes a neigh
An angry eye, a movement – all spirit signs
Wood spirit wake, yield your tale we would say:
Spill a rhyme, a riddle
It's all a game
'Glocken … spiel' we might call it
But

Here just the carnyx calls
Announcing change.

Who was 'tarmint from fox', Lucco?
Ah, I remember – the little scout
Pretty girl
Shame her head

Chose a log to lie on
My horse found her guilty and that pretty neck was so sweet for the
    axe
Oh, if I could only reach the stirrup king's daughters,
Just one, give me just one.
No wonder Mercia's Offa is barred from Karl's ports
Karl would never allow a daughter to live just a horse ride from
    me!
I have my waterfall of tears and here I am the beast.

So no more clothes for burning?
Let the beacon burn bright tonight.

A fool's doublet – you think you will remember him in a year
Like I remember my brother?
His head is here locked in my heart,
I own all property in … that … place.
Pharamond's Salic law will find no way in!
It's another reason to complain
But when will my time come for applause?
Of course when I win the race!

Verden, Germany – Descent to Hell

They had been at sea for three weeks and at last the Cornish vessel entered the estuary of the river Weser close to the seaport of Bremen. As emissaries for Cornwall, Gavin and his entourage had delivered a mission request on first landing in Bremen for onward delivery to the great King Karl. This North Sea port had been closed to the English because of a proposed marriage suit disagreement between children of Karl and the Mercian King Offa. Offa had died in 796 AD, followed swiftly by his son Ecgfrith, and now Cenwulf had succeeded to the powerful Mercian throne. The Cornish had been allowed to continue with a ship's pilot to Verden where King Karl's formal authorisation would be awaited and the Frank court's representatives taken on board for the final journey down the Weser to Karl's battle camp at Paderborn. Gavin's entourage consisted of twenty men at arms, a dresser, a falconer, grooms, two court clerks and translators, two feudal captains and their supporters – ten armed men. With a purser, cooks, slaves and ships' hands the combined force numbered fifty.

Gavin knew that the Cornish duchess Gisela and her family had strong connections along the Weser River. As a young girl betrothed to the Duke of Cornwall, she had brought to Cornwall several fine horses as wedding gifts from the famous Verden bloodlines. Bloodlines were Gavin's concern as the Cornish vessel reached the junction of the Weser and Aller rivers. Verden was just a short distance along the Aller and here the Cornish were put ashore by the Frank pilot to recuperate from their long sea journey. The Duchess's family interests were not to be part of Cornish discussions. Gavin wanted to distance the Duchess from the Saxon families and an earlier disaster that had struck the Saxon powers in Verden. Whilst the Duchess had wished Gavin well on his mission she had not given him any correspondence for onward communication to her family.

The mission was clear: to engage Karl in a treaty and obtain his support against the mutual enemy, the Saxons in Britain. Gavin found the Franks threatening and unpleasant. Despite bringing them warm greetings penned by the Duchess, he found that these Weser Franks inhabited a dark and dangerous world. They had been directly involved in the beheading of 4,500 Saxons in 782 AD some years before, an infamous act of genocide committed when local Saxons in Verden rose against Karl and later refused to convert to Christianity. Saxon turned on Saxon; now years later Karl's Saxon opposition had risen once more and King Karl had marched to suppress them at Paderborn.

As the representative of a pagan state, Gavin found the first meeting with the Franks was difficult; he had no formal experience with the Frank court. The ceremony of greeting was before several hundred local chieftains and their supporters. The Franks viewed the Cornish, their weapons and their decorum suspiciously. Both parties shared the rich cultural experience gifted from the old Roman Empire. The Franks had annexed part of that vast empire, their court in Aachen was a centre for cultural study and Christian teaching and they owned a fabulous treasure hoard enriched through the recent acquisition of the famous Avar treasure.

Gavin needed to find an area where he and his host could find some assurance of his trustworthiness and usefulness to the Frank kingdom. His first topic was to inform the court of how well the blue horse bloodlines had performed in Cornwall. Next he reported on the mineral industry, confirming to the Franks that his lands were still a good source of tin and that gold was still being mined at the Roman mine in Wales. He updated his hosts upon the major conflicts, particularly the advances made in the east of Britain by the Saxon tribes. Gavin expected renewed conflict with the Saxons and he admitted to his preferred allies that the Duke's former ally, the Irish, was no longer the chosen partner for the Cornish.

How could the Cornish pay for weapons and men? asked the Frank chieftains. Gavin advised them that the castle owned a spectacular treasure hoard recovered from ancient wrecks. The Cornish would have no problem in raising a tribute.

The Frank hosts were pleased with Gavin's mission; they announced that feasting would commence and that the Cornish were to relax and enjoy the entertainment. The women were beautiful, thought Gavin, fine, blonde, statuesque.

On the second day of feasting Gavin stood in the long hall at Verden without his entourage; he had been granted a personal audience with Karl's representative. It was midday; not even a guard was present. Gavin could see high into the timbered beams and turning his eyes low he could view the earthen floor. No sound, absolutely no sound; well, perhaps the faintest of sounds as the timber building recorded the sun's heat upon its exposed beams – a sort of tap, the queerest of sounds. Gavin strained to hear the sound of a bird or hoof but nothing, just the movement of the building as the sun swelled in the sky and the wood was tempted. It was then that he noted a disturbing discolouration of the earth before him. A reddening stripe – why had he not noticed it before? Here in the great hall he could make out patches of different colour. He stiffened; how long did they expect him to stand here waiting? The great sword he carried was still in its scabbard. He tilted his head upwards, straining to hear … Just another tap and then to his surprise he noticed a blood patch like a footprint appearing, a blood patch oozing before his very eyes. He drew his sword. What sort of wizardry was this? With his sword he picked at the earth and viewed the reddening tip of the blade. He scratched his head and more blood appeared on the floor beside the first patch – another footprint. Chilling, he began slow backward steps towards the hall's timbered sides; he would rest his back against the timbers. It seemed impossible, but as he made these backward steps the blood trail followed. He stopped at the side and touched the timber frame, allowing his fingers to feel the grain. Silence prevailed, yet he could clearly see steps in the blood trail that had followed him. Something was wrong. Then the noise of a door as a guard entered at the opposite end of the hall and gestured him to follow. Returning his sword to its scabbard, noting the stained tip, Gavin stepped back over the floor, his feet following the darkened earth. Was it real blood or had he imagined the whole thing. The earthen space had yielded a secret. How many heads had been chopped here? The hairs on his neck prickled. A smell was noticeable. Afterwards he likened the smell to being in the presence of a boiling cauldron of body parts.

'Gavin – of course you would like to see our horses,' said Karl's representative as the Cornishman entered the side chamber. 'We have arranged a visit.'

As they left the building and headed for the horsepark

Gavin mentioned nothing of the prints he had seen appearing on the earthen floor.

After three days of feasting and joviality, Gavin obtained his authorisation to proceed to Paderborn where the great Christian king Karl had agreed to meet him to discuss a treaty.

Leaving the town moorings with the Frank pilot, Gavin reminded his hosts that he would see them on his return; he was interested in purchasing a stallion for the Duchess, so they should seek out a suitable animal for him to approve. With its inhabitants waving farewell, the vessel returned to the junction of the two rivers and turned south towards the heartlands of the Saxon people now under renewed attack from Karl's Franks.

Each day, the Cornish, accompanied by their Frank companions, put ashore to purchase food while Gavin's falconer took the opportunity to exercise his bird of prey.

The Duchess had owned Gavin's hawk. 'How many have you sent to their deaths?' Gavin remarked one day with a searching look at the hawk. 'What different sounds do you use for guilty? And now innocent?' He gesticulated with his hands as if transferring a balance. 'Soon you will join a man whose verdict has affected thousands; you will need to accommodate his language.' He looked deep into the hawk's eyes. 'I don't see your ears, hawk!'

The bird didn't respond to any of Gavin's questions. I wonder if Karl talks to birds, thought Gavin; perhaps he has a translator.

Gavin had spent a month in the Frank kingdom and met both Frank and Saxon alike, some as chieftains and many Saxon slaves. He realised that the Saxon slaughter at Verden had occurred because the Saxon tribe had refused to discard their pagan charms and beliefs. They had rejected all advantages and protection offered by Karl; this opposition to his authority had driven Karl's need to prove that Saxon power was inferior to his own and at Verden he had committed genocide. Whilst the Saxons held no fear of death, Karl sustained the seed of a weakness. This weakness was the need to replicate his present order and position after death. Christianity and the form promoted by the Pope offered Karl the retention of that status, and his rule far into the afterlife.

Gavin did not fear recognising Karl as his supreme feudal leader. Karl would not be present in Cornwall. Cornwall's ageing king and duke allowed Christian priests admittance to Cornwall. The rule of law and justice administered in Cornwall by both duke and duchess were a problem area. Ryd, Gavin's own brother, had meddled with the Duchess on justice, and Gavin was in no doubt that the administration of justice would become a trigger point for disagreement. Ryd's position with the Duchess remained a concern for Gavin; would the justice problem flare again during his absence? Acknowledgement of Karl as emperor and allowing the development of the Christian church were small prices to pay for the treaty. And Morwenna? There was no need to discuss Morwenna; she could be part of a tribute and that would be left for Karl to initiate. Karl was interested in gold; he owned his church; he wanted to acquire more treasure, more influence and more subjects to pay tribute. Gavin had to ensure that Karl would seize this opportunity to promote Frank power in Cornwall and Gavin had to promise the Cornish pagans they would not suffer the fate of the Saxon folk at Verden. Gavin would be kissing the King's ring, but the King had no authority to make him submit to the Pope.

Paderborn – the Stirrup King's Table

Gavin's abiding concern whilst in Paderborn was to seal an allegiance with the King, gain the treaty and depart. Gavin had heard of the Pope's problems in Rome and it appeared that Pope Leo was already housed near Paderborn under the King's protection. Gavin wished to avoid any meeting with the Pope; his resolve could have cost him his life.

Gavin was taken to Karl's camp and accorded all the dignities of a worthy ally. He was introduced to the King's supporters and the many foreign court representatives attached to Karl's camp. Despite the proximity of an enemy army, Karl enjoyed the festivities and entertainment provided for his soldiers. Gavin viewed the weapons and power of the Franks; their cavalry were a fearsome attack force.

After the feast, Gavin received his audience with this king of kings.

'I hear you have a great treasure,' said Karl with a smile.

'It is true,' said Gavin, 'yet your treasure was accumulated through battle and great deeds. Much of our treasure has come from vessels shipwrecked upon our rocks. Many have tried to attack our castle and steal the treasure but with our corridor of death the treasure remains safe.'

'You will need to give up some of your treasure if you seek my approval on this treaty,' returned Karl. 'So you wish to prevail against the Saxons; you have already seen they bow to no authority, they fear no man and they believe they are positioned close to the supernatural, they despise my Christian God and you tell me they are proving troublesome in Britain!'

His comments were attended with much laughter from his supporters. 'Why, their horses are easier to subdue,' he continued.

'Great King,' said Gavin, 'we would like to present a gift – a hawk, a specimen worthy of the greatest of kings; you will see its prowess. Call your falconer so that we may bestow the bird into his protection.'

Karl accepted the gift; the hawk was adorned with a gold anklet and a beautiful hood spliced with gold.

'Ah, enough gold to attract the eyes! A fine specimen and truly worthy of my household. Later this week, perhaps tomorrow, we will put our hawk to its first test. We shall enjoy festive pigeon on our table this week!'

Karl was well pleased with his gift. He continued, 'I hear that in Verden you seek a blue stallion; let your choice be my gift for your duke and of course the learned duchess who guides your bloodlines. In fact on your return you could provide me with stock from your herd.'

'With a treaty agreed we will provide you with a tower of blue horses,' promised Gavin, unaware of the impossibility of this promise for the Duchess.

Karl was tempted, or had he planned such a request? 'You shall have your treaty, and now entertainment. My minstrel Agen, you'll meet him later, will accompany you on your return to Cornwall. He will be my eye and ear on your problems with the Saxons and arrange collection of the tribute on my behalf. Agen is a master of languages; he will master Cornish. He will welcome a journey to the land of giants, and your dragon kingdom – Arthur's shield displayed a red dragon, didn't it?

'Uther Pendragon, Arthur's father, fought under the banner of the red dragon,' replied Gavin. 'At our castle we show the burg and the beast but we will try to accommodate

Agen's visit with a viewing of both dragons and giants. He will enjoy his stay.'

'Ah,' cried the King, 'first more entertainment, then you must see my animals; I have some special pets!'

The entertainment was varied and promoted the King's invincibility. There were trials of strength and courage. Often the King's champion was called to participate in trials such as arm wrestling. After the King's champion had defeated the opposition Karl would enjoy showing how easily he could defeat his own champion in a final closing duel. Combat included combat with animals. This seemed to be a firm favourite with the Franks.

Later Karl and Gavin met again.

'What are you building at Castle Winswood?' asked Karl. 'Tell me about your ships and your artisans – we need craftsmen for my building plans at Aachen. And do you require anything from me?'

'As seafarers we have one interest,' said Gavin; 'my brother Ryd seeks Greek fire.'

'We have fire, a fire to destroy all pagan monuments, but it's not Greek fire. I hear that in your lands Christian priests like Petroc are safe and happy living among pagans. Here this would not be possible; we have chosen to completely destroy pagan monuments, like the tree "the Irminsul" on the river Diemel; I destroyed that legendary pillar more than twenty-five years ago. Now that sight would have inspired Greek fire!'

'Is that how long the wars with the Saxons have lasted?' queried Gavin.

'In 772 we destroyed the Irminsul, then we passed laws to halt Saxon cannibalism; that was in 782 and the same year some of them regrouped. Widukind their leader continued to prove a problem and at Verden one group of Saxons assembled to aggravate our armies. 4,500 were put to death at Verden. And as you can see it's almost the turn of the century and the war continues. My advisers have considered alternatives, one of which has been to transfer some of the tribe to other regions. The merchants in Verdun sur Meusse have moved thousands of slaves across Europe; perhaps as many as 10,000 have been moved, passing through transit camps like that at Sachsenhausen near Frankfurt. Verdun is our kingdom's central slave auction site. Any who want a Saxon woman should look there. Somehow we must alter the power and tilt it in favour of our forces; continual war has no benefit for our kingdom. Dispersal of the Saxons even to Britain improves our chances of gaining a lasting peace.'

Had Gavin heard the King correctly? Dispersal of the Saxon power even to Britain aided Karl in his attempt to organise and rule his kingdom! Perhaps Karl would prefer a weakened Cornwall, a Cornwall incapable of holding the Saxons at bay? Saxons arriving from the Weser lands reduced the pressure upon the Franks. The desire for the movement of a disruptive force far away from the Franks made sense.

The next day the King's new hawk performed superbly; three pigeons were taken on the wing. 'Winswood, I shall call my new hawk Winswood; look at the eye, now fear that eye!' The bird settled peacefully on Karl's glove; Winswood had a new owner!

Karl was delighted and he moved across the grass towards Gavin. 'A fine hawk, Gavin, a bird worth a ransom!' Returning the bird to its hood the King viewed the golden pieces and the bird's gold anklet. 'Welsh gold?' Karl enquired. Gavin looked startled.

'Sire, we have no current access to Welsh gold,' said Gavin.

'Perhaps not the main trade from Carmarthen to Rome, but did you know of the disappearance of this season's convoy? The convoy that should have contained the Irish princess Morwenna?'

'I was unaware, sire, that the gold galley had not reached Rome and I have no knowledge as to where the galley and the escorts can be. My brother Ryd was shipwrecked on an earlier convoy and he attended the present season's convoy before unloading at Castle Winswood with Morwenna. I understand that she was taken sick. Morwenna is safe at Castle Winswood. However, with the decision to halt the tribute payment to the Irish she remains our ... guest.'

The King turned to his hawk. 'So would Morwenna be safe with you, Winswood? An Irish pigeon safe among hawks? No matter, Agen will advise me. Gavin, tomorrow you can visit the site of the Irminsul; I shall be readying my followers for another visit from the Pope!'

Gavin felt uncomfortable; no secret could be held from this monarch; he was a hawk observing from a great height, capable of killing all prey, all parties.

Karl's Monologue and the King's Fool

The greatest king in all Europe paced his tent. The Pope was due to visit Karl shortly. The King's concerns emerged as he debated the direction he should take:

What's mixing in this bowl, this night sky, what mixture stirs and
*   signs*
Doubts?
When did I ever doubt my resolve against Saxons?
How many men must be sacrificed before rings can be shared?
I need more treasure. I need gold.
And where does it lie?
With the Avars? No, I have that treasure.
In Spain – I have closed on their gold and silver – an Arab sent me
*   an elephant – a diversion?*
In Wales – close to Cornwall, they have gold.

This Cornish opportunity places my forces close to Welsh gold and
*   gains me an ally*
An unexpected ally against the Saxon.
Together we can press the Saxon west flank forcing them to add
*   men from the east.*
That leaves me ready for gold.

In Cornwall they have – tin
But it's their castle treasure that interests me,
Since they are starved of artisans and knowledge.
'Greek fire' they seek – we all seek Greek fire and
Advantage.
What will my nobles find in Cornwall?
Wives, horses – ah, the sacred blue horses,
And I'm promised

A tower of blue horses!
Yet
They are all pagans
Unbelievers
There lies my advantage.
And the Pope here
Under my protection.

When my warriors receive his blessing
No Saxon will roam these Weser lands again in
Freedom.
None of their pagan charms will succour or defend them against
*   our sky!*
This pope, our pope will reign again in Rome
Supreme.

And whichever family opposes me? I will cut a splinter from their
*   wood*
And burn
Burn their wood till just charred remains evidence their passing.
And then a crown, crown as emperor
Holy Roman Emperor
And when this pope reacquaints himself with Rome he shall place
*   the crown upon my head.*

And should we disagree – on appointments, property – the unex-
*   pected*
Well I'll share, I'll even share my hawk!
And we'll dine on pigeon
And I'll ask the Holy Father
For
Victory.

Now show me a sign, let me see a sign
Let me see rings!

'My lord, his Holiness approaches' – the King's fool announced the Pope's presence.

'He comes – I'll show him my elephant
No, I'll show him this game of chess:
White forces against black
Castle, knight, bishop and
Queen.
Some kings make little movement on a board, yet queens …
Are queens loved more than kings?
And what queen could claim a dragon's head?'

'A dragon queen,' answered the fool.

'Cornwall, it's far from here
I'll send a fleet
To secure the tribute.
I want no contact with dragons
All my rings I've shared
And even unto death God
Will smile at my will and testament.
Perhaps he sees me now
A smile, a charm
A ring no doubt.

'Ah, fool, tell me – which castle is impregnable?'

'Everyone knows that must be Castle Winswood,' said the fool.

'Castle Winswood
And how do you know that?'

'I spoke just a moment past with Winswood,' giggled the fool.

'*Winswood?*' *queried the King.*
'Your hawk Winswood – and a fine specimen of a bird it is. Fly a hawk over any castle and it will tell you all you need – better than any priest or informant.

'His holiness approaches,' whispered the fool.

'Pope Leo was master of the wardrobe – the treasury – before his appointment.
He knows about treasure.'

'Does he know about hawks?' cautioned the fool.

'He doesn't know about Winswood.'

'Well, then we must show him later,' confided the fool.

'Fool, I am well disposed to this Cornish treaty.
Our ally will continue the pressure upon the Saxon and we will be paid in Gold.'

'Good enough for a pope, a gold ring for a pope,' the fool whispered.

'Your Holiness …'

The Irminsul at Marsberg and a Cauldron of Blood on the Diemel

The Great Karl had urged Gavin to view the destroyed shrine to Woden at Marsberg in the valley of the Diemel. 'You can see what we have done to their shrines,' he had cried. He wanted Gavin to view 'winner's justice'.

Gavin was unsure how he would react viewing the destroyed pagan shrine. His expectations were that the tribes would have chosen the site carefully. The Irminsul had honoured Woden and the god's moment of rebirth upon the ash tree. The holy place would have been large enough to entertain a large body of people. The tree or the pillar would have been of a great size. You would expect dwellings for folk who attended the shrine and sold wares to people who visited the sacred place.

That night, as they journeyed up the flooding river, they camped in the Diemel valley. Gavin had a dream. He recounted the dream to his guides:

'After leaving the river bank we made our way up towards the sacred circle and before we entered the cleared area there were faces all around us. Faces whitened by face paint, shaped as if enclosed in wooden masks. Faces and eyes followed our small company until we alighted upon their cauldron.

'A cauldron of boiling penises! Perhaps there were other body parts, but the penises were clearly visible and the soup – if you could call it a soup – was bright red, there could not have been a redder colour; it was scarlet!

'The trees now seemed to gather and draw closer, the sky

grew darker and darker, all I could see were ashen faces peering through the trees. I could only imagine this point as being a descent into hell! Each figure held a great spear; they must have been fifteen foot or more, twenty foot in height, and then suddenly the sky opened to a crescendo of explosions, thunder and lightning, rain fell in sheets and the sky was the colour of pitch.

'After a pause our little band emerged into the sacred circle, there was nothing, the water was pooling, we all feared we would be struck by Thor's blades amid a symphony of destruction!

'"My lord, do not venture further into the circle," my weapons man pleaded. "The god is present, we must leave this place, this shrine is not for us; leave the Diemel now."

'I melted back into the woods, staring eyes no longer focussed on me. Our men were protected. Had the eyes seen us we would all have been killed. Then I heard my brother Ryd's voice, "Turn back now, turn now for the Weser! Do not view the Irminsul; I need you at Winswood."

'I knew that I should proceed no further. I had no need to view the Saxon dark force. Dark forces were at Winswood and Ryd had called on me to return.'

Whether it was due to the plume of smoke announcing a presence or indeed Gavin's dream, the Franks were confused by Gavin's decision to go no further. But they relented and turned the vessel back towards the Weser.

A hawk soared high in the sky – watching.

Wednesday, Woden's day! The water, the holy water was stirring. A great wind was blowing, not a wind to break and destroy; it was a wind to note a presence, the being, a pagan god was present. A heron flew overhead to land by the water.

Later this same heron sprang back into the air – what had interrupted the bird from its feeding?

'What concerns you about the shrine, Gavin?' asked Axel, Karl's guide chosen for the visit.

'I had a vision, an omen, this shrine has no connection to me. You have brought me here and I am concerned that your problems here do not become my problem. To a Frank this site has no value, I can see why you have chosen to destroy it,' replied Gavin.

'We have destroyed the site in order to reduce its power, to reduce its unifying capability over the Saxons. The Irminsul attracts Saxon unity, it provides them with protective powers; they believe that with Woden's protection they are invincible,' said Axel.

'The site and location are clearly spectacular; there is some vibrant energy present. Perhaps it resonates from earlier conflicts,' suggested Gavin.

'Across to Paderborn and north, we have the Teutoburg forest, famous for the defeat of the Roman army. Marsberg, it means the war hill; this is where the energy, the protection emanates to bring the Saxons victory. Perhaps we should build our own Christian shrine upon it, but we don't have an acquiescent local population,' announced Axel.

'You wanted to know my concerns. I am not advantaged here. The Saxon powers come here to be advantaged. I feel I will be cursed should I view the desecration of their monument. There is a dark force present and I do not wish to disturb it. You can feel the forest powers, the veins that link to an underlying deity. Their shrine is desecrated. Woden's tree Yggdrasil destroyed. I will not risk a curse,' continued Gavin staunchly.

Axel shrugged. 'They are cannibals, they eat human flesh,

we need to subdue the tribe. Of course there are Saxons who have moved to other lands like Britain. To break their power we must pursue them. They will have their stories, their battle hymns; unless we pursue them we will never be safe. These Saxons cherish their relics, their sagas, they will remember the protective powers of their shrines and the healing the shrines afforded – just destroying these energy points will not cause the collapse of their culture, unless we chase all of them into the sea,' he enthused.

'I understand you took that approach in Verden. Four thousand five hundred persons put to death because they would not convert! Perhaps they feared they would lose the afterlife promised by their priests,' countered Gavin. 'Immortality and a place at the table of the gods; what greater compensation does a warrior ask? Come, let us take some mead and return to the Diemel,' he added.

One could not doubt the presence of darker powers that looked down on the two adventurers, Gavin and Axel.

'You should be careful you bring no dishonour to your warriors. Dishonour – you cannot charm away dishonour, it breeds a tarnished mindset, once processed and cast—' Axel was interrupted.

'Karl has avoided dishonour, but his captains, his generals, the very act accomplished here has consequences, and you are correct: unless you purge the region of all Saxons, their unity, their courage, their protection will remain,' admitted Gavin. 'The roots of the great tree may have burned, but the view remains. The contact points to the Teutoburg massacre are intact. A resonance right through to the vein and the source of the pagan god's power is ever present. Here on the Diemel I have learned of Karl's Christian ambition, his influence and his control. His control stretches even into the afterlife; I see him astride his horse, stirrup proud, matching the vision of any pope!'

The watercraft bearing the Cornish took to the middle of the stream and made for Karl's port. Eyes followed the craft, but were they Franks or Saxons? Had Karl used the Cornish party as bait? Gavin's vision of the scarlet cauldron and the ashen eyes in pursuit disappeared in the wake of the Cornish vessel. The roots to Karl's Saxon problem remained here deep in the ancient forest; although the tree had been removed, it had symbolised the presence of the supernatural and that remained despite visits by the Franks and the Cornish.

Return to Verden and the Saxon Back

The voyage along the Weser from Karlshafen was uneventful. Still flying Karl's flag for protection, the vessel returned to Verden, through Höxter, Minden and Alapa, reaching the home junction with the river Aller. Gavin had much to consider. He had the treaty and the protection Cornwall needed against the Saxons. However he was worried by Karl's ferocity towards pagans and what he had witnessed. The genocide at Verden due to the Saxons' unwillingness to convert and the continued deportation and transportation of thousands of Saxons to other regions underlined Karl's determination to destroy Saxon influence, particularly pagan influence. So when would Karl insist that the Cornish convert? Was Karl in fact playing with the Cornish? He knew about Morwenna, and at Marsberg, at Wodan's shrine, Karl might have used the Cornish as bait to provoke an attack on Gavin and his entourage.

But Karl had no knowledge of Gavin's troubling visions, only his departure from the shrine. Gavin in an earlier dream at the start of his journey in Cornwall had seen a robed figure kneeling as if about to be struck. In front lay a skull and behind the kneeling figure was a woman, a woman with her back to the dreamer, her naked body unmoved by the disaster taking place in the central scene. The dream was clearly connected to Verden, but who was this woman? His return to Verden would perhaps solve the mystery.

Gavin resolved to view the stallions selected by Karl's court representatives in Verden and choose which one he would accept for the Duchess in Cornwall. Four horses had been brought to the viewing arena and after putting them through their paces, Gavin considered his hosts' opinions. His preference was to choose a stallion that had already proven willing to be transported by river. Since the voyage would last several weeks he had no wish for the animal to misbehave; would the beast need a companion in order to remain calm? A young slave girl was engaged in showing the animals and appeared particularly attached to her charges.

That evening Gavin asked his hosts to arrange some female entertainment and, with the women provided, asked how he could obtain a Saxon slave to accompany him back to Cornwall.

Many Saxon women had been dispersed to holding camps and Gavin enquired of where he could view one such camp in Verden. Here he would choose a suitable companion to tend to his horses and accompany them on the return journey. Of course the girl would not see her family again; just like the Duchess she would be leaving Verden for Cornwall.

He viewed the women presented and asked which girls showed an aptitude for riding and gaining a horse's trust.

Then in an unusual request he asked to view their backs.

In his dream he had viewed the back of a Saxon woman and he asked each one to reveal her body from beneath her robe. The slaves acquiesced and before he had moved forward to view he found himself stifling a gasp. One girl's back had been tarnished by an unimaginable scar; this was no scald, no blade wound, this was something sent from the gods!

On the left-hand side of her back behind the armpit the broadest bend of a red river appeared. A blood-red river. This river, shaped like a reversed question mark, travelled south to join the girl's vertebrae about two hands' breadth from her seat. This great river, now three fingers' breadth in width, was joined by the occasional tributary. Looking back up to her armpit, just one hand's distance from her neck he saw a vast knot of tributaries, all sourced at the knot. These tributaries with minor streams and brooks spread right across the upper portion of her back to the right-hand side of her body. Below these northern tributaries lay a great white plain, a desert untouched by the wounding scar until the desert's southern section and her vertebrae reaffirmed the river's presence. It was a fearful tale, yet a tale of survival from a force that was always programmed to kill. Why had Thor relented; what protection did this girl enjoy?

Gavin moved forward. 'This one.' He pointed, closing on the girl that had been licked by a dragon. 'And what is your name?' he asked.

'Petra.'

Was this the woman of Gavin's dream? Gavin's vision had demanded that he view each girl's back and now he had made his choice; the imagery of this girl's searing experience had an attraction that held Gavin spellbound. Some strange force had taken control. He ordered that the slave be purchased and removed from the transit camp. Now attached to the Cornish entourage she was taken to their quarters and Gavin's hosts were asked to obtain the necessary clothing for the girl to undertake the long sea voyage to Cornwall.

That same day the young woman, who must have been about twenty years of age, had an audience with Gavin.

'The horse I'm looking for comes from a special bloodline,' he said: 'the bloodline known by your elders, the horses that frequented the sacred groves. Have you heard of these things? Do you understand the ways of the horse?'

'I have seen, I have had visions, but know nothing of the

sacred animals that you seek,' replied Petra. 'The old customs are just dark memories, the Franks destroy our culture and our clans – you know about the Irminsul? The Verden massacre?' she added.

'Of course – I came near to the Irminsul and realised its importance. But here on the Aller there must still be special places and special horses,' he answered.

'You tell me your duchess came from these parts; surely she would have chosen a sacred horse to accompany her – you may already have one in your possession,' observed Petra.

'I don't deny that we might, but her stallions are blue stallions, not grey,' said Gavin.

'What you really need is someone who understands the language of the horse. Even if the sacred horses existed, you don't think that the Franks would have allowed us to keep them; such horses would have disappeared,' Petra assured him.

'Yes,' said Gavin 'and it's true that what I need most is someone who understands their language.'

'I am that person' she said. 'I understand their language, I will tell you what it all means, I can administer their justice!'

Gavin was astonished to hear this admission; at last someone who could interpret the way the horse was used to determine justice – just like the Duchess!

'And the stallions chosen by my hosts?' he queried.

'Let's just take a foal, take the smallest, and what name shall it have? What do you call your river in Cornwall, a great river?' asked Petra.

'Tamar,' said Gavin.

'Then we shall choose the smallest and call it Tamar,' she replied.

*

And three weeks later, as if released by Poseidon, Petra stepped into the surf at Winswood leading a young grey stallion called Tamar.

Gavin had no reason to applaud; he was still wondering how to comment on the latest news Agen had brought from Paderborn, July 799 AD, for delivery at Castle Winswood:

'*The Pope was enthralled by the Cornish hawk, its beauty, its speed, its killing power; Karl gave the hawk to the Pope! The Pope promised to crown Karl emperor, Holy Roman Emperor – imagine Karl to be crowned emperor in Rome! What a triumph for Christianity!*'

Why had Karl chosen to pass this message, why the transfer of the hawk to the Pope? Was there some link to the misappropriation of the gold convoy?

Gavin chose not to speculate on what Karl's intentions might or might not have been. He had the treaty and now they could check on the progress of the ransom communications that would lead to the release of Morwenna. First Gavin had presents to deliver and the stallion was to be taken to the castle and properly introduced to the people of the Kylgh. The secret of Petra's back was hidden, hidden from the light.

Marriage of the Dark Forces

How do you explore a dark force? If you have evidence of its potency how do you control it? Do you dare release it? Dark forces were those referred to by the Reader when he undertook each year to analyse the blade of ice and interpret the bubble, the secret. Are secrets only safe when they are kept on ice? What sort of dark force accompanied the Duchess?

In Gavin's absence Ryd had avoided contact with the Duchess. On the second day following his return from Africa Ryd took the accustomed route to the bathhouse from the castle. This was the very route taken by mistake late one afternoon by his wagoner. The castle had special routes for the transport of heavy goods. Since danger came from the port a speedy route was needed to take weapons and men down to the port. Another route was used solely for bringing goods up to the castle from the port. In effect the castle enjoyed a one-way routing system. Ryd's wagoner had travelled the wrong way down one of these routes and for that accident where folk had been killed the Duchess had sentenced the wagoner to death.

Ryd was walking the same route down to the bathhouse. He wasn't under the same obligations as a wagon driver. It was late afternoon when he arrived and after he had taken a few words with Mallor to ensure that his chosen slave was dressed for an outdoor ride, Mallor procured the necessary outer clothing and the girl Kambon paga was ready to join her master. Ryd took a flaming torch and they both descended the stairs to the beast's cell. The hyena appeared to be sleeping. Kambon held tightly to Ryd's arm. Kambon made a strange sound to the hyena. '… Ha … Haaa.' Her white teeth favoured this light.

Ryd wasn't going to explain the layout of the labyrinth. She should realise it was a dark and dangerous area. No one was safe. Through another passage towards light they came to a stable area where a groom found Ryd a mount and, with Kambon seated in front of him, the two moved west across the park towards the entrance to the corridor of death.

Kambon the black slave had covered this route on her first wagon drive up to the castle from the port. Instead of descending to the port Ryd made for the Coombe River crossing and then began to ride up a cleft, a steep cleft away from the death corridor. The movement of the horse pushed their bodies together, the sun was warm, Ryd released his left hand from the reins and engaged the warmth of the slave's back. His hand felt for the scars, for the map and excitedly his hand travelled over her body. Kambon made no movement. This was an unusual experience mounted on a horse and the cleft's tricky terrain was a challenge even for an experienced horseman like Ryd. They reached the top and here they found some woodland stretching out beside a stream. Ryd halted his horse and his hand reached further round to clasp the front of the slave's body, feeling for the scars between her breasts. Both his hands now occupied this space, moving slowly around each nipple; he was breathing against her neck. He released her and she sprang from the horse and stood quietly to the side, leaving her clothing open, showing parts of her ebony skin.

Ryd tethered the mount and with an arm around his slave moved deeper into the wood. Here amongst a stand of beech trees was a yew tree; this tree stole his attention and he stood Kambon in front of the tree that had already flowered early for pollination.

In his shirt on a length of leather was Cai's ring brought all the way from Africa; all the forces were present and ready for an experiment – what had Ryd planned? His fingers touched the iron ring and he sat on the ground. It was at this point that Kambon decided to flit off into the stand of beech trees, hiding behind the trunks. Ryd cast his eyes around the stand, following the slave's movements. She made scratching signs on each tree, an animal marking each trunk. Wild, that's how her play could be described, and her wildness increased as she discarded her robe and naked slipped between the trees.

The yew watched, its branches motionless, but from behind the thickest of its layers there emerged the tiniest of whispers, or was it a chant: 'A pie's ghost, tarmint from fox, a vole's beard, the gloat from a Doyle … tarmint from fox?'

The ring could be seen through an open vent in Ryd's shirt. Ryd's eyes tracked the movements of his naked cat. And then suddenly she was beside the yew. 'No,' shouted Ryd. 'No, no.' Kambon had rushed amongst the leaves and seemed to wish to put them into her mouth.

The slave stopped running and looked perplexed at her master's warning. She pointed at the tree foliage and shook her head. Ryd shook his head too. Her African dark force was oblivious to the dangers of the dragon kingdom's most notorious poison, the poison from the yew.

Joining her, with his arm round her protectively, he moved deeper into the forest. Finding a shaft of light pouring through the beech branches he laid her on the forest floor. His chest touched her naked breasts. His fingers traced the scarification across her body, down from between her breasts across her belly; these strange African shapes were unimaginable on a white woman. Her fingers rose and wandered across this intimate part of his own body, copying the shapes on her skin and awakening in him that moment of supreme invocation. She gathered him into her body; the leather holding the iron ring checked the ring's progress as it bounced between their two bodies from white to black. His lips took her nipples into his mouth. He was stiff, hardened, ready to pursue her map, to travel every turn, ready for every gradient, the treasure was warm and waited, he pressed hard, his mouth and tongue moved to engage her lips and as he moved deeper into her spot her welcoming thighs tightened upon his body. Her lips parted and she arched her back, tightening her stomach to accept his storm delivered deep inside her; his moans evidenced complete pleasure. Pleasure of yielding to a dark force.

This was untamed wildness. She had taken the white knight, consumed his passion, their trunks had pursued the route of an ancient tribal ritual and now their bodies were subdued with perspiration. She had learned of the peril of the yew and she had learned when to yield and favour her slave master. She had asserted a power over his dark force but she wondered if she would ever be allowed to return to the light.

Ryd was released from one of his burdens. He gazed at the ring held to his chest by the leather; he had released one force from within himself but would another force flee the ring? He resolved to return to the bathhouse and hide the ring. He would need assistance; Kambon would keep the hyena occupied while he hid the ring in an old treasure container hidden in the beast's cell. Of course Kambon had no idea of Ryd's intentions. She returned to the saddle and they began the descent of the cleft to reach the entrance to the corridor of death before entering the stables below the bathhouse.

Once more they took a torch while Ryd found another for Kambon. Taking the leather thong holding the ring from his chest, he showed the ring to his slave; they then returned to the beast's cell. The animal was awake, its wild eyes in consternation at the presence of the two blazing torches. They were alone in the labyrinth, just a wild hyena, Ryd and his slave. The lock was pushed and the beast manoeuvred itself to the back of the cell, pushed back through fear of the fire. Kambon joined Ryd in the cell, showing no fear and holding her torch aloft. The treasure container was found and the ring inserted into the clay vessel. Again it was returned to its hiding space, and both the torches released their shadows from the cell. The beast confused and tense in its corner relaxed. The dark forces had been held at bay. This time the danger dissipated, the anger predictable, but for how long can you restrain a force that's waiting for any opportunity to escape?

Part 3

Twenty-four Hours

Ring or beast?
What did you see?

Princess Morwenna, and Gisela, Duchess of Cornwall

In the summer of 799 AD, alone in her cell at Castle Winswood, Princess Morwenna, the ransom princess, mournfully considered her dilemma:

The sun sets, its fire dissolves into a metal pool
But where is the pool?

Night beckons
And on this dragon shore
Not a single word
Nothing from my clan nor the Holy Father
Does no one consider my fate?

Gold, it was surely the gold!
We were too close to Lundy
Seen by its hawk
And now with the beating of weapons in this evil castle
I fear every footstep.

I have just one companion
He labours about his cell
I remember him passing my door and later his song floated my
*   way, provoking our gaoler.*
The whole castle learned of our music interlude
Now no words leak from his cell
Just scratching each night
He fears the day
He fears the rush
We both fear Winswood.

So no matter how my life unfolds
And if I never soar free – to conquer these Winswood heights
I've shared a prisoner's sorrow

And formed an image
Of a face
But what will be my fate?

Oh to escape
Oh for water … water …
Each spilling drop
Counts …
And I count the days, weeks …

Hark
I hear … footsteps …

That summer evening, the slave girl Petra had been sent by Gavin to carry out a check upon Morwenna. Petra had crept along the hall outside Morwenna's cell. Now hanging in the corridor for a brief moment like a moth flickering in candle-light, she placed her ear against the cell door.

Moments later a guard, seeing Petra flitting back along the corridor, stopped her. 'Petra, Duchess Gisela asks if you have checked on Princess Morwenna.'

'She is quiet,' replied Petra, 'I listened outside her cell.'

Within days of arriving at Winswood, Petra had been charged with some of Morwenna's care. This was decided after the Duchess had taken Petra to view the 'waterfall of tears'. This fifty-foot fall was eight miles north of Kilkhampton across a yellow moor to the west of the Clovelly road.

'My father sent me with the horses, the blue horses to Cornwall – a
    wedding gift,' the Duchess had said.
'Of course I could interpret their sounds from an early age, and I
    built the herd, this sacred herd.' (The Duchess had pointed at
    her horses.) 'From the Cornish I received a hawk. I listened to
    that bird and learned as it soared
High above castle and crag seeing everything;
This is a feared castle and will remain so
 An outpost, far from the Weser, far from the Rhine.
'Folk whisper that all this is the realm of the dragon and that I as
    dragon Duchess rule!
Let them so believe,
Winswood is a treasure castle – castle of fear.

'Do you hear, do you hear the falls? Come, come right to the edge.'
(Having dismounted from their horses the two women had peered
    over the edge of the precipice into the freshwater spray formed
    as the water crashed fifty feet onto the beach below.)
'What … what worries you, Duchess?' Petra had asked cautiously.

'My horses,' she replied, 'I'm worried for their future
I am responsible for the bloodline, its purity,
I am responsible for interpreting their souls
And I'm worried for my authority, my words – Ryd challenged my
    justice!

'One of his men, his team, a wagon driver was accused
He had travelled to the ladywell, and ran down a girl
I had him thrown from the cliff, the Henna cliff!

'Cihtric – Ryd's father – never questioned my justice.
The Duke is often absent
Cihtric sent Ryd from Winswood for fear!
It's my justice
That has been the way at Winswood.

Ryd wished to move away from the spirit word, my word, he
    proposed a system where
Men only serve!
And now Morwenna has been drawn among us – a Christian
    princess in a dragon land!
So "my duke" demands a ransom … and Morwenna waits …
    waits on pagan justice.

'You ask me what worries me – crossing my judgement, opposing
    the old ways. It's a provocation and this new system of religious
    belief; Morwenna's Christianity with its leader a pope far from
    these shores, that can only lead to war!'

'If she represents so much danger kill her,' Petra had replied.
    'Powder the yew … a simple potion …'

'Ah, it's such a long time, we use the crabs now, the bodies fall and
    the crabs – snip and snap.' The Duchess had gestured, using
    both hands.

'Human flesh, the flesh of our enemies, I have eaten it.' Petra had
    nodded. 'I just hear screams.'

(The Duchess had looked away from the spray and gazed far out to
    sea.) 'And I just remember the smell, the burning of the
    Irminsul, I carry it forever and I only hear the beast.

'I've brought you here – you see that island? There.' She had
    pointed to Lundy.
'Behind Lundy is Wales, Wales and gold! That island is where
    everything turned.
Morwenna was snatched from the gold convoy off that island. The
    gold didn't come here, just the beast!

'That island, sometimes it's hidden … by mist, a cloud, just like a
  secret.
The secret will always reveal itself
Under the right conditions.
Lundy's forge fashioned the sword Excalibur. That sword was the
  key to a secret – the passport to a great treasure.
Lundy's giants are our staunchest supporters; that will never
  change – the island of Hercules they called it in ancient times.
Lundy is loyal to us, through the seasons, through all the storms,
  all the disturbances.

What are you like with weather? Simple weather – can you advise
  me, keep me informed, be my hawk?'

The Duchess's meaning had been clear to Petra. Here by the
  waterfall the Duchess and her whispering society sought to
  recruit Petra; what choice did the slave have?

Petra had peered back towards the fall and its spray and turned to
  the Duchess with the words, 'I too am an outpost, far from the
  Weser, far from the Rhine!'

And as she had looked back at the Duchess something distant had
  stirred in the young slave's memory, the slaughter at Verden, the
  scream!

Unbeknown to the women an aged druid, the oracle at the
  waterfall, had observed the Duchess and the slave. 'I wonder
  what they saw?' He had laughed, refusing to move closer from
  his hide. For the men he always proffered his hand and asked,
  'Ring or beast, what did you see?' For the women perhaps he
  should have asked, 'What did you hear?'

If Petra had seen any strange transformation observing Lundy
Island she never revealed the insight. She remained diligent in

her work; she continued to carry out duties for Gavin but she 'listened' for the Duchess.

'Now that the princess has settled for the night I won't be returning until tomorrow,' she said to Morwenna's guard. With that remark delivered somewhat tartly, she slipped past him in the corridor, almost bumping into Lucco, the Duchess's dwarf, who was closely observing her, boldly casting his eyes over her body. Petra glared at the little man. 'Uh,' she muttered to herself before returning to her own quarters.

That night's heat was oppressive, yet some folk at the castle were plotting and planning and thinking about the next day, because it was a special day, the feast day for the great horse race.

The Race, August 799 AD

As morning dawned, the feast day welcomed the Duchess's celebrated horse race at Castle Winswood. This was the day when blue banners were suspended all over the castle walls and folk came from far and wide to observe the great five-mile race. Conditions for racing were not ideal. The ground was hard. The race was always a dangerous test for horse and rider. This year Ryd had returned and the old rivalry with the Duchess's horses would be repeated. The Duchess was expectant of another victory. There were representatives from Wales present to cheer their own champion. Thousands of people were scattered across the treasure hill feasting and enjoying the entertainment.

The race start in the bowl of the treasure hill was packed with supporters. The mead had been flowing all day, the sun shone and by mid-afternoon everyone was ready for the race to commence.

The Duchess and her retinue enjoyed a special platform from which they could attend to the start and encourage the riders at the finish. Cihtric was amongst the Duchess's company; Cihtric remained responsible for the security of the castle and its folk while the Duke was away in Bodmin. The robed Reader sat with the Duchess.

The only viewers of the race from start to finish were the hawks soaring above the castle heights. Beyond the castle and through the town the race would cut out along the Clovelly road before turning west to the sea. Even the hawks would have difficulty viewing here as the horses made their way down through thick oak foliage to a cleft, before two water crossings of the Coombe River returned the riders to the treasure hill, a distance of five miles.

Betting fever mounted, in addition there was Cornish wrestling, bear baiting, cock fighting; it was one of the greatest festivals in all of Cornwall. It was an opportunity … to be attacked. Yet with so many Welshmen and Mercians present enjoying themselves with the Cornish one could understand that attacking the Cornish would also mean attacking their friends, those who had travelled to celebrate this spectacular horse event.

The castle shone, exalting its blue banner racing achievements. Some of the horses were sweating, final bets were placed and, after a short speech of encouragement from the Duchess praising the ancient Verden bloodlines and the Duke's patronage, the riders moved to the start.

Part of the crowd threw their spears in the direction of the riders to accompany the signal to start, which was given by one long blast of the carnyx. Ryd was bunched in with the leading riders as they spurred towards the castle walls and the shouting spectators. Next the riders headed out through the town and were lost to viewers on the treasure hill.

If an early advantage were to be stolen it would happen here in the town. Groups of riders with one patron such as the Duchess would attempt to obstruct their competitors and enable one of the patron's riders to secure an early lead spurring out north on the Clovelly road. Most winners needed to establish an advantage in the first mile and be first to enter the cleft, which appeared at the three-mile point with the first glimpse south on the Lee mound 400 feet above sea level returning towards the great castle. Some riders preferred to remain out of trouble but by the time the leaders had reached Lee the lagging riders would have no chance of success.

The Duchess's champion Canton had managed to gain a couple of lengths on Ryd and another five riders before clearing the Clovelly road westbound for Stursdon and the cleft. The cleft slowed every rider and care was taken as the competitors urged their mounts down through the oaks. Here in the oaks they were hidden from view. Here the Duchess had conceived the idea of hiding an archer.

The leaders raced down through the trees and it would have been a difficult task to establish which one was Ryd, which one Canton. The hidden archer waited and waited, choosing his moment. 'A fillow of grush, dwallow from a moan to curb Ryd's cackle,' recited the archer and he unleashed an arrow towards the foremost rider. It passed unseen through trees but glanced at the last moment against a bobbing bough to miss the rider before embedding itself in an old oak.

Ryd was aware that an arrow had passed and he checked his horse for a moment before angrily spurring the beast forward. By this time Canton had stolen an advantage. Ryd appeared to be hesitating. Had he lost the urge to win? Weapons men could be seen watching through the trees but neither archers nor arrows disrupted the racers again.

The 200-foot descent through the Lee cleft to the wood yard and upper ship build area continued fraught with danger. Canton was making good his advantage, it appeared that he couldn't be caught, he just had to hold his place across the river and head for the adulation that awaited every worthy winner of the great Kylgh race. Ryd was challenging two other horses below Lee; no observers would have suggested that he had a chance until in the river Canton's horse suddenly became snagged. It was a net. The horse had been snagged in a net. A great commotion took place; Canton fell into the water. Ryd avoided crossing at the same fording spot and with great good fortune emerged on the opposite bank of the river to screams of joy as his supporters saw him coming first into the treasure fields. Ryd had won and he punched the air in triumph.

The Duchess was shaken; white in the face, she was seething with rage. She cast an angry look at the Reader and then gave a half-hearted salute towards Ryd. Ryd wondered where Lucco might be. This was his third triumph and he would be receiving the Duchess's golden feather. The feasting would continue long into the night. The townsfolk's favourite had delivered; he was champion again. Ryd was safe for tonight, just tonight.

Midnight, August 799 AD

Midnight that same August night Gavin and Ryd were standing upon the battlements of Castle Winswood almost 600 feet above sea level, looking across the Coombe valley towards the sea at Signal Point.

'See the stars, see there a shooting star,' said Gavin, blinking as he looked up from the distant sea line into the night sky.

'A sign, it's a sign I say,' confirmed Ryd.

'A sign, by some we sow, and by some we weep; know you all their names and locations? Why, in a thousand years do you think people will say it's a sign, brother?' questioned Gavin. 'A sign that you would win the great race!'

'For me it's a sign,' concluded Ryd; 'it says the ransom ship is near! I grant that some will miss this hurtling spark asleep in their beds, but others will worry and probe their mystics! The race is no longer a concern for us. The ransom is now the central matter; it's good that we haven't drunk too much mead. But I grant you that it's not just a sign that we need, it's a direction. Anyone can kidnap a sign. You need a direction. The sign dictates the need for action!'

'Well, the witching hour approaches and the Duke's in Bodmin ... Father is asleep. What do you fear, brother?' continued Gavin. 'The Reader said someone would arrive to harm Winswood.'

'A broken blade, famine from a lost harvest, the ring. Oh, and of course the Duchess's justice,' said Ryd.

'Well, for me it's thirst, Ryd – here, take a draught.' Gavin offered his brother some water. 'Ah, that ring, where have you hidden it?'

'It's hidden where the beast sleeps, below,' said Ryd, pointing out across the valley, 'below in the bathhouse cages. Do you remember the hidden pot in the floor we used for treasure when we were young? It's in that pot.'

'You said a dead sailor lifted it from another's finger – it's just an old iron ring with some rune upon it, you say ... ah, signs, but what is the direction?' joked Gavin.

'It's a pledge, I think. I heard Cai mention a pledge, and since then everyone who has worn the ring has died,' Ryd reminded him.

'So there's a curse upon it, and if you fear it, why have you brought it to Winswood?' Gavin demanded.

'Because there is a force within the ring and if we can gain control of the force we will merit its power.'

'If! Can its power rival that up here? What do you fear here?' and Gavin pointed at the stars.

'I can't touch the stars,' said Ryd, 'so if I can't touch or feel I hold no fear, but if they rained down upon me ... why, I would die, or perhaps with luck I'd be saved. Neptune saved me, the water god, and I fear him and I'm marked, like one of our blue stallions, marked with stars and curved moon! Marked for a king's ransom or a king's tribute ... nay, brother, you are the star gazer, you were chosen for the journey to Verden with our tribute for Karl, and look at that beauty, that Saxon slave you brought back, Petra; no, you are the chosen one. Why, I'm surprised Karl didn't baptise you – instead he left you a pagan, and here we are counting on his help, Karl the warrior leader of the Christian world; he is one we should fear!'

'And enemy of the Saxons like ourselves,' interjected Gavin.

'I'm ashamed – this dilemma with the Irish princess,' Ryd responded, 'but after my time with the Vikings and the gold convoy I could not refuse them ... their prize ... especially since they honoured me, a parting gift, a maid to ransom. And she on course for Rome and holy orders! I had no idea she would be removed from the galley.'

'Father's best hawk and our promise to return a tower of blue stallions diverted Karl from any ransom problem with the Irish,' admitted Gavin; 'besides, Karl must set Pope Leo III back on his pedestal and subdue his own Saxons. The Christian princess – a mild confusion – Karl's interest is only treasure and tribute, I swear; why, he took sixteen oxen loads from the Avars. No girl, not even a Christian girl is of any importance.'

'Granted, but an Irish chieftain's daughter and bound for Rome,' Ryd said with a smile.

'Brother Ryd, you give me no credit for the treaty and my negotiations; I have my skills. This is our opportunity to face up to the truth. The Irish are of no use to us against this Saxon menace. Karl's position is clear: he either murders them if they don't convert, or he transports them and sells them into slavery; 10,000 Saxons have been moved in this way. He destroys their relics and their sacred places – he destroyed their tree the Irminsul!'

'But you didn't see it!' Ryd reminded him.

'I wasn't going to trust Karl at the shrine – I had a vision, I took no chances, I needed to return quickly. What if the Duchess had turned on you again, who would champion your position?' questioned Gavin.

'Father and I will counter the Duchess. Was the vision your authority to bring that Saxon girl to Winswood?' Ryd queried.

'She will prove attentive to the Duchess; that will help you, and I need a good translator,' confirmed Gavin.

Ryd laughed. 'Ah, a translator of dreams; careful she doesn't become your nightmare!'

For a moment Gavin hesitated. The horrific scar on Petra's

back flashed into his mind. Triggered, should he tell Ryd? A sign had attracted Gavin, and just as Ryd had returned with the ring so Gavin had returned with Petra. Was Petra certain death for someone at Winswood?

'When you speak of nightmares do you refer to the Duchess or Morwenna?' Gavin asked. 'Morwenna will be free soon and peace will return to Winswood.'

Ryd grimaced. 'Peace? The Pope holds our hawk – an omen; there will be no peace at Winswood until we all convert and until then we risk his Christian ferocity. I have seen the followers of Islam, I have seen … and so Karl fights fire with fire … I have seen … the beast! The beast will leap on your back, puncture your skin and wound, it will sign your back in claw and blood!'

Gavin noticeably reddened. 'Is that reason to convert – fear?' he responded.

'Fear of Karl, fear of his Pope – I don't fear them and I don't fear the Irish, but I'll feel better when the Irish ransom arrives and we're rid of Morwenna,' Ryd concluded.

'So will it be tonight?' Gavin asked.

'The witching hour stirs,' repeated his brother.

'Tonight, it will be tonight, watch for the fires – father's training and the alert fit well. In the early hours we'll see treasure – you saw the star – I agree it's a sign for someone somewhere. Be they Christian or pagan, it's a mark, we all saw it, and now we wait, we wait,' announced Gavin.

At this moment their father appeared on the castle heights.

'Father, what brings you out?' called Ryd.

'Ransom,' he said, blinking, 'a dream, I woke and like yourselves I'm nervous. This is a special moment, we take a great risk … will the Irish deliver, with this moon will they come?'

'Your dream, Father, what was the picture? We've just seen a shooting star; what did you see?' questioned Gavin.

'A crown,' said the old man, 'I saw a man wearing a fabulous crown – I've never seen such a crown before – and a face, a face which spun away as if on a wheel, then the image disappeared in a watery ripple.'

'I wonder what our reader will make of it. Perhaps another journey,' said Gavin with a smile.

'This might foretell a journey for all of us and not where we expect. The crown was anointed ... with orbs, globules of gold moulded onto each point. The crown was firmly fitted ... why, the picture could have been from the head on a coin except that the face ... it was real and I thought it would speak to me, then it started spinning, spinning and I woke,' continued their father.

'A spinning coin, that's a symbol of treasure. Shame that you lost the face before it could speak – lost treasure or perhaps a warning,' surmised Ryd.

'Our treasure, is it about our treasure?' asked Gavin.

'Shall I wake the Reader, Father? This may be important,' said Ryd.

'Are you sure the crown was of gold and not of thorns? The Christian Jesus had a crown of thorns,' said his brother.

'No ... this was a crown to fill any treasure room, part of a hoard, and it sat firmly upon a man's head. We are king ... ah, I'll leave you with your shooting stars; perhaps the figure will return,' said the old man, and he left his sons to continue with their own observations.

Ryd gazed back at the stars. What had Ingvar said? Golden horse sentinels guarded a treasure so vast that to move it you would need as many camels as there were stars in the sky. No, he wouldn't tell his brother about the city Silas had seen or mention the treasure map and route to it scored into his black slave's back.

The Signal

The castle was still; Cihtric returned to his room and was welcomed by his wife.

'You've returned; all is well, Cihtric?' asked his wife.

'A shooting star was seen, and I'm still seeing that crown.'

'Ah, the crown – you're still troubled,' his wife said. 'I've never known you so worried, not since the Reader considered the blade of ice in January. Now it's August, instead of bubbles appearing in ice we have crowns.'

'I hope you are not mocking me. The bubble fastened upon a secret, a problem that would need to be addressed; perhaps it refers to the Irish maiden who waits to learn her fate, or the minstrel Agen, sent by Karl – the Reader said an enemy would come within the Kylgh, within our circle. Our clan could be overthrown, never have we been in such danger, and the Duke in Bodmin,' sighed Cihtric.

'And what is the Duke doing in Bodmin?'

'I can tell you what the Duke is not doing: he is not attending any Christian meetings. He is in Bodmin to see our giant Wulfgar secure the Cornish wrestling prize – he's taken fifty men with him,' Cihtric reported.

'Fifty good men that we may need for our defence,' retorted his wife.

'Are you suggesting that a Cornish wrestling contest could benefit an Irish intruder?' Cihtric asked.

'And why not?' responded his wife. 'You are the commander concerned with timing and signals. Here is one such timing opportunity – the Duke is away, far from our beaches, demanding the attendance of our strongest men. A summer feast day has now been enjoyed with men full of mead and wine, most of them unable to provide a proper defence – is that not a timing opportunity for the Irish?'

Cihtric drew a breath. 'The Duchess remains at Winswood. We can deal with the Irish; it's the foreigners that concern me. Foreigners should be watched, the Reader said. Cart builders, weapons men, silversmiths, ship and figurehead builders, Vikings, Danes, Mercians, Welsh, they are all foreigners, they are all here! The Reader says loosen their tongues – why, we haven't even found one tongue, except the locksmith and he's in the tower with the princess.'

'Leave it to me,' said his wife, 'I'll find you a tongue … if you … if you …'

In another part of the castle, a weapons man lay in bed with his wife.

A signal – a long burst on a horn could be heard all the way from Signal Point along the valley right up to the castle where a general call to arms was announced.

'The signal, the signal,' cried the wife.

'Oh how I hate this – in bed – and now a rush to the corridor of death,' complained the warrior.

'Be thankful you heard the signal, be off or the only death will be yours. You've slept; be thankful you weren't in the fields,' rejoined his wife.

'It's August; if I'd been in the fields I'd be full of mead and be playing with cherries,' said the warrior, extending his arm, reaching to play with his wife's nipples.

'Bah – home guard,' scolded his wife, slapping his arm away. 'Give me a professional soldier any time; they understand the call to arms, immediate action, they protect their women … firm stomachs and fine biceps …'

'I'll protect you, my dear. Before you can count to a thousand … let's see how fast I can reach the bathhouse. I'll be back before dawn if it's just an exercise … ah, those cherry maids.'

'We'll be with the animals,' said his wife, 'ready to herd them through the slave stockade … ready for—'

'Say nothing; I can't bear the thought of you being so close to the enemy,' complained the warrior.

'And how else shall we defend ourselves? If our men fail, what price our lives and our animals?' his wife asked.

'Let's pray we don't have to use the herds, first let the enemy discover my arrows,' the warrior responded, adjusting his clothing and leaving the room.

In another part of the castle, Agen, Karl's representative, lay asleep. Gavin descended from the battlements in response to the alarm and rushed to the minstrel's room.

'So, minstrel, wake up,' Gavin said.

'What is it?' Agen yawned.

'The signal, you must wake; perhaps it's the treasure ship, the ransom, but for your safety we must move you to the cells,' responded Gavin.

'But why?'

'My father says it's safer for you. If we are attacked and lose, the enemy will find you in a cell. You will be saved since they will presume you are our enemy. If my clan or I return you stay free. Look, Agen, if, if we lose and an enemy sees you walking round this castle you will be killed along with the rest of the Cornish guards.'

'And weapons, my weapons?' asked Agen.

'Leave your weapons here. I'll put you in a cell next to the princess; she's the cause … well, you know about her, you might speak with her. But mind you give her no reason to think you are friendly to us.'

'Did I not hear sounds earlier from that tower?' Agen questioned.

'The torture rack – loosens every tongue. We fear a secret society. Our mystic prompted us after speaking to the Duke to attend to the locksmith. My brother suggested the threat would come from another quarter, a music maker – think of that!'

'What did he say?' queried Agen.

'He said the minstrels and the jesters that travel between the great courts spread discontent and ill will.'

'And the locksmith, where is he from?' Agen parried.

'Not from here, but he is a capable man, opening and closing *all* doors. He certainly knows most of our secrets. We need to learn all his connections – every link to every society. What better than to torture the man for a day? But we must be swift, I must attend to the signal, come.'

Agen remained mistrustful but chose to accompany Gavin to the castle cells.

Back in Princess Morwenna's cell the young girl woke to the sound of the horn.

'That signal, a long blow on the horn: should I fear or should I rejoice?

'They tell me they wish me no harm, but what is harm? Months circling a cell with barely one visit each week to the ladywell, their bathhouse – full of pagan women, slave women.

'And escape – no one escapes Winswood. Each day I hear the baying dogs, a torture bell and then screams. Screams as each body is dismembered. This evil town with its treasure and dragon rocks.

'And slaves, we heard that slaves were traded, for horses,

gold! This is a slave town and not one Christian; where are the Christian Cornish?

'We Irish once provided them support in case the Saxons attacked; we would attend their flank and they would pay a tribute. This was dishonoured just as the men who forced me to these shores have dishonoured me. I have no maids, no attendants; how can I even follow or find my God? '

At this juncture, the young girl turned towards her window and the view out to Signal Point.

'Oh for a little more moonlight!

'Only when I view the sea and the point from my window does my belief return that I will be saved. But with the moon comes the night, the night and footsteps. Oh for Father's hand to deliver me from this castle and quell my fear of footsteps.

'Footsteps
I hear footsteps again
Footsteps

'They return
STEPS
WINSWOOD … A CURSE ON YOU!'

It was Gavin.

Gavin announced himself while unbolting the cell door. 'Ah, little princess, the alarm woke you. Here, a present, from the Duchess; she will visit at dawn,' and he opened his hand to reveal a small wooden doll. 'There is no need to worry, it's … an exercise, and we have another Christian prisoner; he'll be next door to you. Curse? Did I hear you say curse?' Gavin's mind returned to the image of Petra's back – had he taken the right action by bringing her to Winswood? Would there be no release from his secret? Without waiting for Morwenna's response he closed and locked the door.

'Here, in there, minstrel; we will speak later,' Gavin ordered as he directed Agen into the adjoining cell.

'Bring me water,' Agen reminded him.

'Later,' said Gavin, slamming the cell door. 'Well, two Christians on the same floor; I wonder what music they will make?' he muttered.

'How do you expect me to sleep with a general alarm?' asked Agen.

'You'd be mindful to sleep; no one has ever passed alive through our corridor of death. Thousands of arrows descend and the few still alive spill into the spear pits. You won't hear their cries, just the baying of dogs,' said Gavin as he turned away from the door to Agen's cell.

Agen allowed his buckle to fall to the floor, and then lay upon the bed. The moonlight gave the cell a little light; far below the dogs could be heard joining the general alarm. It wasn't long before he heard a knocking at his cell wall; it was the princess.

'Are you the Christian?' the princess asked.

'I'm Agen, minstrel to the court of Karl in Aachen. I am a Christian.'

'Have you come to help me?' she sobbed.

'Of course Karl stands to aid all Christians,' Agen answered.

'But what brought you here to these pagan shores?'

'Tribute and treasure, I'm sent to learn of a great treasure.'

'Ah, the treasure,' the princess sighed.

'Is it possible that this pagan land conceals such a valuable treasure?' Agen asked.

'If it exists it will lie in the treasure hill.'

'Were you there?' queried Agen, scrabbling closer to the cell wall.

'It lies below the bathhouse, below the slave girls, in an underground vault close to the jaws of baying animals: there lies the treasure,' the princess responded. 'It's no secret.'

Coughing that spilled from a neighbouring cell interrupted their conversation.

'It's a locksmith; he is in the cell on the other side,' said the princess.

'And why is he a prisoner?' asked Agen.

'Perhaps the locksmith should tell you himself, but first how is our pope?' countered Morwenna.

'He fled for his life, Pope Leo, he fled Rome and crossed the Alps. I left him at Paderborn with Karl – have no fear, Karl will see he returns to Rome. You were lucky,' reported Agen.

Morwenna gasped. 'How was I lucky?'

'Had you not been kidnapped your vessel would have arrived in Rome and your lack of protection through the Pope's hurried departure would have led to your immediate imprisonment. Here at Winswood you are close to your clansmen; this signal could result in your freedom,' Agen responded.

The coughing continued.

'Please allow me, Princess, a word with our locksmith,' said Agen. 'Locksmith, do you hear me? Is there no escape from Winswood?'

The locksmith with a muffled voice murmured an unintelligible reply.

'Ah, he makes no sense,' admitted Agen.

'He has been tortured; it is lucky he is still alive. Later when we have more light, and if he recovers, perhaps we can press him,' said the princess.

'Of course, in a few hours,' yawned Agen, returning to the rough cell bed.

Waiting for the Irish

Above the 'corridor of death', beyond the sanctuary, there was a checkpoint where warriors were counted and given weapons and supplies. Three men were readying themselves for action.

'I've counted 200 men with full arrow packs all ready for the corridor; another hundred men and we will be ready for any encounter,' said the troop teller.

'Good job it's a warm night – I'd give anything to be in the bathhouse now,' said Uffa, the first warrior to have arrived.

His comrade answered, 'Are you mad? You know the orders: all female slaves must be at the bathhouse whenever we have a signal alert.'

'That's what I mean,' said Uffa, 'I'd prefer to be at the bathhouse.'

'You seem to have forgotten that if any of our male slaves are seen in this corridor our orders are to signal the bathhouse guards to commence the slaughter of the female slaves, every single one. And you wish to be in the bathhouse?'

'Not a soul will reach this end of the corridor, with all our pits, arrows and the herd,' Uffa replied. 'The slaves would never try it.'

'The signal is not your responsibility,' his friend reminded him.

'You make too much of it; you won't make that decision without the clan chief. Anyway, as I said, no one will pass this way save ourselves,' Uffa was adamant.

'Fire straight, brothers, and keep me from your worries; with enough men allocated for 2,000 arrows already and another 3,000 in a matter of minutes, my concern is timing,' interjected the teller.

'You know the distance,' the friend said, '3,300 yards from Signal Point to the sanctuary here. You have just thirty minutes to allocate 500 archers above the corridor starting at 2,300 yards. Already you have 200 archers in place. Do you think these foreigners will sprint to their deaths? We have plenty of time for the corridor to run with their blood. Mark my words.'

'One day they won't come up the corridor,' the teller replied.

'This is the only quick way to Winswood, under the eye of our hawks; this is the way they will come.'

And Uffa's friend was correct.

At the sound of the signal all the castle female slaves had to make their way to the bathhouse, also known as the ladywell. Often this would take them close to thirty minutes before they could assemble and present themselves to Mallor, female head of the bathhouse slaves.

'Why are we all here … a sacrifice?' asked Petra.

'The alarm signal; are you not used to this by now, Petra?' scolded another slave called Utta.

'Since my arrival this is the second time I've heard the alarm horn but this is my first visit at night to the bathhouse. Will we get an all clear … soon?'

'That's if it's a friend,' replied Utta, 'but if it's an enemy they will keep the first horn blowing and light fires to count the enemy vessels.'

'Do they have enough wood to build fires for one hundred vessels?'

'You mock our predicament, Petra; if just one man reaches the sanctuary, and if one male slave is seen here the guards have orders to kill us, all of us! In fact anyone in the bathhouse can be slain under this order, so if they move that precious Irish princess here during a full alarm then you know that she too will meet her death,' the slave responded.

'Morwenna, surely not?' replied Petra.

'Everyone – they have no use for slaves or anyone who can turn against them,' confirmed Utta.

'Don't they know how much female slaves are worth? In Verdun, a good female slave, a Saxon slave will fetch a coin or two.'

'Petra, when were you in Verdun? You told me you were from Verden on the Weser,' cut in Utta.

'Yes, it's true, Verden, but everyone knows that Verdun on the Meusse is the slave trading capital of the Franks.'

'These Cornish have no dealings with Verdun, they know nothing of Verdun or the demand for slaves from the Moors. The male slaves at Winswood move heavy loads up and down to the Duke's port. Ah ... but the Duchess keeps you up in the castle ... listen, when you spend more time here at your real work, and she'll cast you in here when she is tired of you, then you'll learn,' said Utta, scowling.

Petra's eyes blazed. 'But this place, can't you feel it ... it's a place of purification, purification before calling the deity!'

'There's no such form of signalling and calling deities here. Purification, ha ... why, this is a pleasure dome for the weapons men! That's of course if they are invited – if you stayed here you would have to quicken your pleasure skills,' added Utta.

It was at this moment that Mallor the head of the bathhouse appeared.

'Slave girl, what skills do you have that we could use here?' asked Mallor.

'I have forest skills; I am learned in the herbs and potions of the forest,' offered Petra.

'Well, those skills will not be needed here; with looks like yours you will never be allowed in the forest, will she?' Mallor asked with a smirk, turning to the other girls that had joined her. 'She'd be grabbed by the pixies, the goblins and any other smart male lurking amongst the leaves, eh?' They all laughed.

'Go and meet the Arab slaves, Petra,' Mallor advised, and Petra crossed the bathhouse to the women from Saldae, including the slave known as Kambon paga.

'Did you remind Petra of our problem, Utta?' added Mallor.

'I did, I informed her, but no one will conquer the corridor of death, least of all a male slave.'

'I heard her mumbling about an ancient rhythm she felt,' said Mallor's companion.

'She probably refers to the druids that met at the ring,' said Utta.

'Was that the last sacrifice?' asked Mallor. 'We can't afford to sacrifice slaves. Who would complete all the tasks?'

'But if the port work recedes or the harvest fails?' asked Utta.

'I thought we were speaking about sacrifice to deities,' Mallor continued, dismissing Utta's probe. 'Sport, luck: well, they sacrifice to that all the time. If you are silly enough to engage them when they are involved with their animal baiting and their bets … then you could find yourself racing against the animals to reach the sanctuary. But she is far too beautiful to waste on such a race … no, that's for the old slaves and our enemy, the Saxons,' she concluded.

'But she is a Saxon,' another of Mallor's helpers reminded her.

'But her children won't be Saxons, and she will be with

child soon, mark my words. Verden, she won't be seeing Verden or Verdun,' said Utta. 'The Kylgh is not ruled by Karl!'

'Karl of the hoard, holder of the greatest treasure in all Europe,' said the helper.

'Outside our hoard,' exclaimed Mallor.

Petra was in conversation with the Arab women, a group that included Ryd's slaves from Saldae and other women who had been found on a wrecked Barbary slaver.

'What sounds can you make?' asked Petra.

'When we learn of a death we make this sound,' said Gul the first Arab, who was soon joined by another of Ryd's slaves.

'Well, I must learn this sound,' said Petra.

'Shall I stop them?' Utta asked Mallor.

The Arab women began their cry of protest.

'Leave them for a moment – it takes their minds away from the alarm. Look to the point for the fire and tell me what you see,' said Mallor.

'One bright fire dancing,' said Utta.

For a moment Mallor was transported back to her childhood. Fires, foreign warriors, this was the reality of life along the British coast. Men were killed, treasure and food taken, the women raped and beaten, some kidnapped never to return. Mallor had been taken aboard a Barbary slaver and only through good fortune had she been brought to Winswood when the slaver had foundered on Lundy. Mallor could no longer remember her home or her family. Winswood was her family; she would always serve Winswood. Before Winswood nothing counted, nothing was certain, her life had been full of fear and chaos. At Winswood there had never been a successful attack on the great castle. Its warriors were feared throughout the region. Winswood had brought peace and stability to her life.

The Arab wail continued its drift across the bathhouse.

'Still one bright fire dancing,' pronounced Utta after another interlude.

'Tell them to stop,' said Mallor; 'we won't hear the horn giving the all clear.'

'Stop that Barbary wail; you're not in North Africa now. We wish to hear the all clear,' said Utta.

'Barbary – what does she mean?' asked Petra.

'It's the name given to the North African region to which Arab slave ships that scourge Britain's coastline return with their captured white slaves. If any such slave ships are caught in Winswood waters the men are fed to the beast,' said another Arab slave.

'Hush,' said Utta.

'And the beast?' questioned Petra.

'You will be fed to the beast too unless you hush!' repeated Utta.

'Where is the beast?' continued Petra, refusing to keep quiet.

It was at this point that the Duchess Gisela emerged from the passage leading to the lower levels where the beast and dogs were kennelled. She was accompanied by her dwarf Lucco.

'Oh my … sorry, ma'am, we had no idea you were present,' said Mallor.

All the slave girls were in terror of the Duchess and all were overpowered by the horrendous smell emerging from the lower depths of the treasure labyrinth that the Duchess had opened.

'Petra needs to know all about our animals,' said the Duchess. 'Come, Petra, we have time; Lucco will show you how we care for our beast.'

The three disappeared back into the passages below the bathhouse.

At Signal Point three miles from the castle the warriors tasked with the safety of the clan and the castle had been carrying out procedures to alert the clan to port intruders. The next stage was to confirm whether the intruders were friendly or preparing to attack. Nine men and a boy called Wolf from a signal complement of twenty were in position. The point rose 250 feet above the port and was known affectionately as the dragon's neck. Near this neck fires could be lit to count the number of ships approaching harbour.

'All the castle folk will be running for their positions, they heard the horn and a single fire has been lit; what are your orders?' asked a signaller called Hud.

'It's a foreign ship, all alone; we will wait. See below, just a few men chatting with our guards; it looks calm,' answered Jard the signal commander.

'Do you want to send young Wolf over the cliff?' Hud asked.

'It's only the Duchess that sends men over the cliff, Hud; well, the Romans had their leap of Leucadia, cliff sacrifices to Apollo. Young Wolf should wait by the signal fire. Look, what are they doing? They make a sign, they are waving torches – it's a sign out to sea! What are the conditions?'

'It's calm, not a breath but ... I see lights, two lights moving, two more ships coming into view,' replied another signaller positioned on a rock promontory known as the dragon's head. The head marked by two ears of rock jutted out from the long ridge of rock just like a dragon's neck; from it a signaller had a perfect view of the sea passageway into the Duke's port so long as the moon remained bright.

'Watch,' Jard shouted, his eyes returning to the quay, 'they are working a deception, look, they have turned the torches on our guards, see their fighting men hidden in the ship well are spilling onto the quay. Light two more fires, full warning horn. We have an hour at least,' he said. 'Their best armed warrior would take ten to fifteen minutes to race up these heights.'

'They make a grave mistake,' remarked Hud the first signaller; 'even with sixty men in that ship they will need several hundred to enter the corridor.'

'What of our two port guards?' asked Challor, an archer.

'Dead,' said his commander.

'Shall I unleash our arrows?' Challor queried.

'Yes, we'll put a few hundred into them; that will make them run for the Coombe. Don't wait for these two ships to dock, let's start the dance,' returned Jard.

'The two ships have set their oars, they'll be on the beach in minutes,' called the signaller from the promontory.

'Are you sure they are Irish?' asked Challor.

'They can only be Irish, ships like that; they've come for Morwenna,' confirmed Jard.

'Then they've come to the castle of death,' spat the archer.

Back on the castle battlements Ryd and Cihtric looked down towards Signal Point, peering into the dark, seeking to discern the signallers' message; would they need to rush for the corridor?

'See now three fires and a full alarm,' shouted Ryd.

'Damn them – they think they can steal their princess,' swore Cihtric.

'How do you know it's the Irish?' queried Ryd.

'August, perhaps they thought we would be full of mead and neglect to post signallers on the point. Of course it's the

Irish; they are incensed over Morwenna's ransom. It's judgement night. We have trained for this. They will run for the corridor. Three ships, well, that's not 300 men and even if they have their finest warriors they have woefully underestimated their task. The dragon's mouth waits to be fed; come, let's join the feast!'

Taking to their horses, they rode the short distance of a mile and a half to the sanctuary end of the corridor of death.

The Battle for the Corridor of Death

An hour after midnight the Irish warriors were forcing their way along a corridor cut into a hillside deep rooted to the left with dense overhanging conifers. Their ranks were pressed together through the narrowing of this channel or chute that gripped tighter the further they travelled. To the left they were unable to climb out of the chute; they could only climb to the right with great difficulty. Their advance, once rapid in pace, slowed. Suddenly fire bales and an immense number of arrows fell upon them. They were too slow to react to the ferocious onslaught and with the Cornish mostly unseen, the Irish force beat upon their shields and held them aloft in defiance. A killing momentum built up, with the air thick with Cornish spears and arrows, until after twenty minutes the Irish faced total annihilation. Hundreds of dying and wounded warriors splashed against each other in the corridor. It wasn't rain; the corridor was wet from human blood.

Hours later as daybreak slowly spread across the corridor the cries of wounded men abated. The killing continued as the wounded were despatched; no one, with the exception of one wounded chieftain, was to be left alive. The Irish force, illuminated by the dragon's breath, now lay destroyed at the dragon's feet.

'How many have we killed?' asked Ruan the teller, standing at the sanctuary end of the corridor.

'Three to four hundred – no one survives this. If you extract yourself from the corridor by clawing your way over the hedge you fall into pits on the riverside. It's not a pleasant sight, bodies impaled upon spears lining the pits,' answered Cranock, the warrior commanding the corridor.

'Order the slaves to carry the bodies away on carts. The crabs will enjoy a fine feast,' said a relief warrior who at daybreak had just joined the battle scene. 'The women will report if they find any Irish alive. I've seen Ryd and Cihtric riding for the other end of the corridor to view the choice; from there they intend to meet up with Gavin above the slave stockade and return to the castle.'

The choice was a cauldron-type position at the foot of the corridor of death. It was named 'the choice' since it was a junction, one route to the right and the slave stockade and the other route straight on to the castle through the death corridor.

Later as dawn spread, castle hawks were seen circling over corridor and cauldron.

'I must report on our men,' said Ruan.

'Some have died, usual places, not enough care cleaning up – half-dead weapons men, you have to get used to finishing them off: spear into the breast, throat slash, don't decapitate them, makes them easier to transport,' said Cranock.

'The women will sort for coin and valuables for the castle, the clothes and chain mail all stored at the port. Weapons, spears, arrows all this end, stored at the horse field store,' the teller reminded him. 'The slaves can deal with the naked bodies; when the ox carts are fully laden, then down to the sea with them.'

'I don't want the women near the pits,' said Cranock. 'I want the male slaves to sort out the pits, dig a channel to each pit to make the body extractions safe.'

'These are all Irish – they were supposed to bring a ransom. That girl's chance to escape Winswood has ended, her life is forfeit; why, even our hawks scream for justice,' remarked the relief as the hawks screamed high above.

'Well, it's not justice for her; she didn't ask to be removed from the convoy and turned over to Ryd, neither did she expect her clan to bring their weapons rather than the gold. What about the chieftain over there?' questioned Ruan.

'He's sport for the feast,' said Cranock; 'he'll be under escort to Winswood by noon – he'll regret reaching the sanctuary end of the corridor. As for the girl, we have lost lives and there's the cost of weapons and defences destroyed; there will be no mercy from the Duke. This corridor of blood won't impress itself upon his memory, but we few, we will remember every mark and splash. No spring water will cleanse this corridor, it will leach blood forever, a reminder of our feat of arms and our love for Winswood – *Onan hag oll*,' he shouted, and the men shouted back, returning his tribute, '*Onan hag oll*.'

Gavin returned to the castle to release Agen from his cell. Loud cheering resounded all around the castle, celebrating the Cornish victory. The noise reached a crescendo as he entered the cells.

'Well, minstrel, it's the torture cage for you,' laughed Gavin, speaking loud enough for the neighbouring cells to overhear.

The princess, aware of Gavin's arrival, interjected with a plea: 'Take me, take me, they have fought over me, not the minstrel.'

'My lady, your deceitful clan have lost the battle, 500 dead,' exaggerated Gavin. 'Under peaceful guise they slipped into our port, later they killed every guard they met. First we must consider our losses. Your time draws near; we shall discuss this matter, be sure of it. For the minstrel other pleasures wait.' Gavin winked at Agen. 'We have a cage.' Opening the door to the minstrel's cell he added, 'Come, you'll be our feast's entertainment!' With a finger on Agen's mouth reminding him to remain silent they both left the cell for the feast room.

Shortly after their departure the Duchess appeared in the same passage accompanied by Lucco, her dwarf; they both entered Morwenna's cell.

'Ah, child, a dreadful night; you must have been frightened, all this movement, these men at arms. You received the doll?' The Duchess had cast an eye around the room, then towards the window and the distant sea.

The princess nodded. 'Yes,' and she pointed at the doll, which had joined the other play pieces that the Duchess had given her. 'Will my torment now end?' she asked.

'You're a Christian, you should pray that it ends, child,' suggested the Duchess. Lucco began playing with some pieces he had spilled on the cell floor: a small black horse and a hare, supplied from a box containing two more wooden objects, a bird and a black cat. He was perturbed but he said nothing.

'As pagans why should you care about me, a Christian girl?' Morwenna queried.

'We all seek the same end, child: certainty of an afterlife, protection, good luck. Whichever spirit or god can supply that need we follow. We haven't chosen Christianity yet; we wait for the advantages. When we are advantaged we too will be generous. Your God must first convince us with victories in battle. This day your forces have not been successful and our horse gods and hawk have prevailed.'

'The guards say you breed the sacred blue horses,' replied the princess. 'You preserve an interest in the horse gods.'

'It's true; I brought the horses here from lands near the Weser River, and since I have no sons or daughters they are my only interest, but the horse gods have long been a preoccupation of the Cornish and not only the Cornish.'

'Do you miss your home country?' asked Morwenna.

'The Weser river lands? Well, I was young, just twelve when my father married me to the Duke. The winters were harsher than here but I had friends to accompany me to Cornwall and we introduced our sports, races, and we took to their hawks.'

'And your dwarf?'

'He was a gift, Lucco is all Cornish,' answered the Duchess, 'but now I must go and attend to the locksmith; he seems to have sustained an injury.'

The Duchess now entered the locksmith's cell to check on the torture wounds.

'Ah, if only I had Lucco to comfort me,' sighed Morwenna.

The Duchess, alone in the cell with the locksmith, left after some minutes and called on her dwarf to follow.

Out of earshot of the cells she said to Lucco, 'I never told Morwenna that I threatened to take your tongue years ago. You will always do my bidding. And now, Lucco, you may attend the feasting. I trust you found me some yew; we will mix a potion, to infuse the drink of Cihtric's wife. I'll need the third nail from a badger, smillow of wedge, a louses's gresh, ah … and a snail's eye; we will mix a portion of boad! '

The Duchess paused; the Cornish may have experienced a great victory but Morwenna's plight could inflame and unite all enemies of Cornwall. The Duchess who initially had befriended the child now stalked the corridors like a beast. She would not allow Morwenna to endanger Winswood. She returned to her room to reflect on her choice of death for Morwenna – a blade or a powdered potion from the yew. Her dwarf began counting as if recording a potion: 'Heel of owl, glued woe, peweled corch, probis.'

The Feast

The clan commander Cihtric, Gavin, Agen, Ryd and a number of field commanders and their supporters were gathered in the feast room. Cihtric sat in the centre, able to hear conversation from most points of the room.

The battle had taken place more than a mile from Winswood in the corridor of death. The tactical advantage of forcing hundreds of men through a narrow chute and trapping them at a distance while unleashing from the forest heights thousands of arrows and fearsome fire bales had resulted in few casualties for the Cornish and the complete destruction of the Irish force. There was no escape from the chute or the spear pits banking the chute on the flood plain side of the river.

The men filling the feast room were well trained in what can only be described as an execution process rightly endorsing the castle's fearsome reputation. Confident, jovial in their victory, it was difficult to find any Cornish who had been wounded since this time hand-to-hand contact had been removed from the combat palette. The deaths had all occurred at arrow distance or spear-throwing distance; the Irish had been halted through a tactical advantage maximising the terrain opportunity of Winswood. It was this chute that Ryd saw as the perfect opportunity to fill with 'Greek fire'; no wonder he had been frustrated not to find a supplier in Saldae. Without Greek fire, Ryd had chosen fire bales to light the chute and spread terror amongst the warrior force advancing up the corridor.

In daylight, the spring beside the chute slowly purged the blood-stained earth. It would be the only reminder of the battle; this earth would forever yield the memory of warriors cheaply sacrificed. Their chieftain had been the only warrior to reach the sanctuary end of the chute, but 'the sanctuary' was not an appropriate name for any survivor of the corridor; those who reached the sanctuary would meet the castle's beast.

In the feast room the tables were set out like three X's that flowed down fitting tightly together, one following the other, like a winning line in the middle corridor of a noughts and crosses game. Cihtric sat at the centre so that he could hear the chatter from the whole company. The tables were soon filling with the clan commanders and their supporters.

Gavin turned to Agen. 'So what have you learnt from the princess?' he asked.

'The young girl is in shock; she couldn't believe her clan would avoid the ransom with this trickery. Of course she fears for her life; what value has she now?'

'No value to us,' replied Gavin; 'she is a liability, the Irish won't pay, her life has been forfeited by today's action, but come, see our cage.'

Ryd now joined his brother. 'So, minstrel, has Gavin brought you to view our cage?'

Before Agen answered, he surprised the brothers by leaping into it. 'An excellent size, but my sovereign wouldn't like to hear that his minstrel was forced to sing from this stage.'

Hauling him out, Gavin calmed the Frank. 'Our duke's fool is in Bodmin; you would make an excellent substitute, Agen, but come, get out of these minstrel clothes.' Gesturing to a guard, Gavin commanded, 'Get the locksmith.' Then pointing to his dresser he turned to Agen and said, 'Agen, we have some finery for you; here are some clothes fit for a noble.'

Ryd and Gavin then moved to the clan group surrounding

their father. 'Father, have you sent word to the Duke at Bodmin?' asked Ryd.

'Of the victory?' his father replied. 'Not yet; we'll wait till after the feast when all reports are in and our reserve forces have arrived. We need to know of the losses at the port and a full detail of any spoils. I don't want to tell the Duke of any losses until I have counted the rewards. Remind me, Gavin, how did the slaves fare at the slave stockade?'

'The Irish moved as we predicted; they were in such a rush to reach Winswood they just tempered their steps for a few minutes at the choice, just twenty weapons men held back until the first shower of arrows prompted them to move up the corridor behind their main force. Not a soul confronted the slaves and no one returned from the corridor, so the animal herd that lay in readiness was returned to the top field at the cliff farm.'

'And the male slaves?' queried his father.

'Like lambs – we could have armed them – they were commanded to make a great noise; their presence and the size of the stockade deterred the Irish from venturing to tackle that camp first. It's just as we planned; at the points of choice, if you time your attack and place the enemy under pressure, unprepared troops take the easy route. They were not prepared to take on the slave stockade but preferred to strike at Winswood through the corridor.'

'I still think we need to build a number of pits up that side,' said Ryd. 'One day some warriors will halt before the corridor and they will sweep into the slave stockade first.'

'And our herds will descend upon them, and with that and the spears from the slaves they will return to the choice,' said Cihtric.

'I still think we need pits and a stronger force with Gavin at the stockade,' urged Ryd.

'With your Greek fire,' mocked his father, 'we could breathe dragon fire down from the slave stockade too!'

Ryd shook his head. If his father had seen the spectacular effect of this liquid and the overwhelming advantage it delivered he wouldn't speak of the Saldae secret weapon with such disdain.

Gavin intruded to make a point. 'We have our horsemen supported by spear-wielding warriors on my side. If I am attacked in force, archers from Ryd's corridor will join me – that's the plan. No one has considered a full attack on Winswood from my side.'

'We have considered that option,' replied Cihtric. 'The animal herds are available to obstruct progress up through the slave stockade.'

On another bench a conversation was taking place concerning the fire bale teams.

'Those two fire bale teams with their bets and their games will one day cost us our lives,' said one warrior.

'What do you mean?' his friend asked.

'They bet on whether the bale stops before reaching the corridor. They bet on whether the bale bounces over. They bet on whether the bale lodges in the corridor. They bet on whether the bale doesn't catch fire. They seem to have forgotten that all the bales should be on fire in the corridor. Imagine what would happen if both teams bet that all their bales would fly over the corridor and fail to cause any damage! That's what happens when the Duke's away – the bale teams strike out and play.'

'If the Duke finds out those fire bale men will be in a queue off the Henna cliff, and that's without those sentenced in the month by the Duchess and her hawks!' said his friend.

'Have you heard what happened to Lucco?' the first warrior asked.

'No.'

'Tell them, Lucco.' Lucco looked away. 'Ha – he couldn't light the first bale – no wonder, too many idiots had been pissing on it after the race. Had to fan it, didn't you? Well, he goes up close and what jumps out? A viper! Didn't take kindly to all that piss. Course Lucco, being so small and carrying a flaming torch, merely had a shock as the snake went for his nose. Well, you should have heard him shriek. He fired the rest of the bales with arrows. Good job you're not taller, Lucco! I think we've cured him of saying the first thing that comes into his head – eh, spollet's grunzel, or is it collet's spinch?' The table erupted with laughter.

At this juncture Ruan the teller arrived to confirm the death count with Cihtric. 'It's 290 dead and the chieftain is alive.'

'We'll feed him to the beast later,' said Cihtric.

'Father, I see that Agen is ready to join us,' said Gavin, observing Agen in his new attire.

'Ah, Karl's minstrel, bring him to me, but first let me hear from Ruan; did we lose many of our own men?' he asked.

'Five in the clean-up process. We need a special group to deal with that problem – it's the greed for personal possessions makes them careless and they pay the price,' said Ruan.

'Why don't they hack off heads before rummaging through clothes?' spat Ryd. 'A headless warrior ceases combat.'

'Ah, that just creates another problem, all those heads looking up; no one wants that, eh, Reader?' answered Cihtric, turning to the mystic.

The Reader replied, 'I welcome our success; our luck and our detailed plans have borne fruit – all fear Winswood. The Duke will be pleased.'

'Well pleased that he missed the fight again,' interjected Gavin.

'Be quiet,' scolded Cihtric, 'you know the rules of vassalage. This is our duty; perched next to the Saxon barrier we risk our lives for this castle.'

'But—' said Gavin.

'We all know that our luck and future lie with Winswood,' interjected Cihtric sternly. 'Here we live and here we will die if the gods choose.'

'Then let us toast our return from the corridor and our victory over the enemy,' proclaimed the Reader.

All the warriors cheered and welcomed the toast.

'And now in memory of our dead – may they view us with honour.' Again a great cheer filled the hall as the toast was proclaimed.

'An accomplished victory, Cihtric,' said Agen, 'but how many men would really test your defences?'

'Fed up of playing fool so soon? Why do you fish for that information, minstrel?' interposed Ryd.

'Well, on the outside you appear to have prepared well; look, there is little evidence of stress in this room. Yet I don't see 10,000 men at arms here at the castle; you must be aware you have a manpower shortage,' said Agen.

'Every defending force needs an advantage,' replied Cihtric. 'The defending force needs to establish a kill point early in the conflict. The kill point is where a kill momentum must be achieved, sufficient to rebalance any numerical deficiency in the defending force. To reach the kill point the enemy will pass along a chosen route and make choices. We bait the choice points in expectation that the enemy will follow the bait. The corridor of death is aptly named. We need ideas like Ryd's Greek fire to maintain our advantage, especially if we lack the manpower to deal with a numerically superior enemy.'

'So the slave town is bait?' enquired Agen.

'Of course,' answered Cihtric. 'The port is bait; the slave town is bait; why, even Winswood is bait. You wouldn't wish to wander around Winswood at night!

'And why is that?' queried Agen.

'The pits, the beast, no one roams here at night – the animals, they guard our treasure,' said Gavin with a smile.

Gavin's remarks were interrupted as the castle hawks were heard calling.

'Ah, feeding time – where's that locksmith? You said to loosen his tongue, eh, Reader? Gavin, fetch him,' commanded Cihtric.

The locksmith and Princess Morwenna had been left unattended in their cells while the guard accompanied Agen and Gavin to the feast room. Both the prisoners had heard the shrieking of hawks.

The locksmith was spurred to call to the princess, 'Please forgive me interrupting your devotions, Princess. I fear for my life and indeed yours too now that your clansmen have perished in the corridor. Do you have a hairpin or a buckle? I made these locks, and if you work away with vigour and dexterity the stone next to the interconnecting door between you and the minstrel can be loosened; trust me, this may be your only hope of leaving the castle. Go now to the interconnecting door; can you see where the locking pin enters the granite? That stone can be freed, but you must use a pin or a buckle from your side.'

'Thank you for giving me hope, but what if the minstrel fails to return?' she replied.

'Then all is lost,' he answered.

'You say you worked in these cells; did you attend to the bathhouse and the treasure vaults?'

'I built it all and I despair of the horrors hidden in the underground corridors of that place,' he said.

'So you know all its secrets?'

'I know all the secrets of the hoard and that is why the Reader has caused me to be thrown into this cell,' replied the locksmith.

'Are there many treasure rooms?' questioned Morwenna.

'You cannot conceive of the size of the treasure; why, I heard that the great Karl took sixteen oxen loads from the Avars yet that is nothing compared to the hoard of Winswood. Under that bathhouse is a vast labyrinth; of course the animals are free to roam below and that's why feeding is so important. When they are fed they can be kept quiet and the treasure can be viewed. But the beast, you would not want to be caught by that animal. They cut the rush to clean the passages, ensure there is no blood. In the labyrinth through a long passage you can join an outside path that takes you behind the slave stockade and makes possible a cliff escape – so through the bathhouse you could escape. Of course if I were with you and the minstrel I would be able to show you. I know how to negotiate the labyrinth,' he replied.

'If he returns let it be done – we will overpower the guard and bring you with us – you have my word,' she said.

Loud voices halted their conversation; guards were returning with Gavin.

'Well, locksmith,' said Gavin, 'our cage is ready and if you survive that perhaps the Duchess will demand the Henna cliff – that's truly a dragon's leap!'

*

In the feast room the warriors awaited their entertainment. Female slaves kept the feast tables filled with food and wine. More warriors had arrived and the locksmith shuffled in to be caged.

Cihtric was still deep in conversation with Agen:

'You have to force the attacker into corridors; last night we used fire arrows and rolled straw bales off a steep hillside through the conifers down on to them. There was no retreat. They met thousands of arrows. The fire threw them into confusion and they sought escape – some clawed their way over the corridor straight into the killing pits. We left them till daybreak; bodies choked the corridor and the pits. Four hours, we waited four hours before daylight spread across the sky.'

'The moon gave them courage; they charged up from the slave stockade. There will be much mourning across the sea when they fail to return,' said Ryd.

'Where were they from?' asked Agen.

'Cork, Kinsale, and none of them will see those shores again,' replied Ryd.

'Their chief, what plans do you have for him?' asked Agen.

'The chieftain? Father, when do we deal with the chieftain?' Ryd turned to his father.

'After the locksmith – first I want to see that locksmith get out of this cage.'

'Here he is, Father,' said Gavin, readying the locksmith for the cage.

'Locksmith, the Reader tells me to be wary of someone in our midst who knows secrets. Well, apart from the family no one knows more of Winswood's secrets than you do,' said Cihtric.

'It's true I know of the treasure but I have not told anyone of the labyrinth or of the roaming of the beast,' said the trembling locksmith.

'Stop. I hear you are good at breaking locks; well, let's see you work on this one. Here, put on this cloak and minstrel's hat.'

'Ryd, spin him off,' ordered Cihtric when the man was caged.

The great cage lurched into the air, hauled up by a rope pulled by Ryd's warriors. The locksmith fell to the cage floor, losing his balance. The cage was slowly swung out on a beam over the castle battlements. Below the tethered beast waited in anticipation.

'We'll leave him to consider his thoughts and … loosen his tongue,' said Cihtric.

'This Irish chief,' Agen said, considering, 'why don't you set him free, return him? He will tell of the folly of attacking Winswood and arrange the ransom.'

'I'm tired of the problem; we have lost men,' said Cihtric, 'and expended thousands of arrows. From the personal belongings we have nothing of value; why, their three ships are the only valuable commodities that have come from this business. The Duke will be angry. We have to replace our arrows, spears, think of the cost. Then there will be the discussion with the Vikings; they will be unpleasant; they are always unpleasant over ransom payments. They will expect a payment since they delivered the girl to Ryd. We shouldn't be involved in kidnap or ransom; it attracts an attack and we deplete our resources. If you kidnap, then expect a swarm of bees, angry bees. These Irish won't share their honey, and if we release this queen, why, she will set up another hive and set that against us!'

'I am no expert on the manufacture of honey,' said Agen,

'but perhaps there is someone else who would have an interest in gaining the freedom of this young bee, this princess.'

'And who might that be?' asked Cihtric.

'Karl!'

'Karl … what interest would he have in her?' asked Cihtric.

'She's a Christian,' said Agen.

'But this was an act of war, they attacked us.'

'I am sure that Karl would have a close interest in her welfare and she could return to his court with me. You could let the chieftain free and tell him that you have passed the girl into Karl's safekeeping. Any costs that Karl incurs, the Irish will pay with Irish gold,' suggested Agen.

Cihtric looked keenly at Agen. 'I like your idea … more, more mead for the minstrel … now a song.'

The Cornish sang their song, 'Onan Hag Oll':

I'm just passing through, coming closer to you
Redruth's my way, then I'll sing about Fistral Bay,
Saw blue bards march the street
Strange voices lapping my cheeks …
Onan hag oll, they say
Onan hag oll …

They sang a few verses before all chanting to hear Lucco. They wanted to hear the dwarf's famous version of 'the blacksmith and the forest hawk', or his 'monkey joke'. Lucco chose the former.

When evening sun and wizard wand unite
To pool cloud islands in a molten set;
As crim and orange rule and discord fight
The forge for thoughts proves harder to forget.
When old Beale sweats his farrier's temper

To draw a shire's nail to hoofy shape for stash
I stay to share a line with Holmsley's fender
And learn of deeds at Ellingham and Melplash.
Then as circling time approaches, this old reel
With tales of choicest meat and produce flowing
Turns, and with youngest Beale – fleshed from filing –
Uphill winds and tunes breath to Winswood Park,
Where in peril of a tax on idling
I dream of lamb and light on summer's spark.

The poem was acted out by the dwarf springing from one table to another and concluded to great applause as he tried at the end to set himself alight, crying out, 'A dimson of mead, a dimson of mead.'

The warriors were debating whether to sing another song when Cihtric was interrupted.

'The artist is here and desires permission to honour our victory against the Irish,' said Ryd.

'Good, send him over,' Cihtric replied, and the artist joined Cihtric on his bench.

'What suggestions do you have?' asked Cihtric.

'Flags, standards, we need to decorate the flags and standards with honour,' replied the artist.

'Our flags herald the beast; are you suggesting we change these?' enquired Cihtric.

'We need to applaud, give thanks to our deities for providing luck, providing the power to influence the choices made by the enemy,' suggested the artist.

'And how do you propose to achieve that? We still have forest spirits whom we call for support – eh, Reader?' replied Cihtric.

'If our men can grasp a symbol, a remembrance of a great victory, they will carry that symbol forward to even more victories,' said the artist.

'Then let it be three triangles without a base. I have seen three triangles in a vision upon a dog's head. A head that had been savaged by a beast,' said Cihtric.

'It will be done. Should we check with the Duke?' asked the artist.

'You attend to your work and I will attend on the Duke,' said Cihtric.

'These flags, standards and signs are all important,' agreed Agen; 'they must be understood.'

'As important for our warriors as for all folk,' said Cihtric, nodding.

'The symbols, the signs have many meanings; none of us can imagine how many stories can be recorded from such a diverse range of symbols, but I worry about your pits and diverse devices that tread upon the warrior ideal. Won't this harm you in your pagan afterlife?' Agen questioned.

'How do you mean? Why should our pits and our desire to maximise the kill have any influence on our afterlife?' asked Cihtric.

'We all have warrior ideals; why, we can trace these ideals back to the Romans and the Greeks. One man and a challenger surely the greatest test. But you use pits and other devices, which do not place one man against a single challenger. Are you not concerned that your deities will disapprove of these procedures, these tricks?' Agen added.

'Would your pope disapprove?' said Cihtric.

'Karl would disapprove,' returned Agen.

Cihtric reflected, 'Of course we would have no need of such devices if we had more men and weaponry in abundance, but we have a finite number of folk who we can feed and who we can put into service. I accept your point – it's hardly a warrior's death to be impaled upon a spear placed in the bottom of a pit. Or to be set on fire by a hay bale tipped from a hillside.'

'Far better to meet an arrow in the breast viewing Winswood from the corridor! Who cares how these folk die?' intruded Ryd.

'It is a concern – honour – is it an honourable death? What do you say, Reader?' Cihtric turned to the mystic.

'I cannot speak for those that are not with us, but speaking for those that are here, warriors expect an honourable death. A dishonourable death must be avenged. If you kill in this way you must expect the hawk of vengeance to observe and return,' replied the mystic.

'So you think we bring problems for ourselves by seeking advantage through weapon trickery?' responded Cihtric.

'To hell with this line of thought; next you will tell me it would have been better to have lost honourably,' said Ryd.

'And what do your women think of it?' asked Cihtric.

'We do not ask our women,' replied the Frank.

'Our women want to see their men return, but with honour,' said Cihtric.

'And how do women fight? Have you seen them? They use every artifice to gain advantage,' said Ryd.

'We don't have the numbers that Karl can muster,' added Cihtric. 'We shall continue to push the barrier of trickery. Why, someday you may be able to cast a spell around an enemy, point a wizard's wand and "poof", they might disappear. Will that be honourable?'

Agen chose not to respond.

'Here women remove the clothes and possessions from the bodies of the enemy dead. That's why we wait until the men are sure there are no survivors, before the women range across the battlefield,' said Cihtric, adding, 'We honour our foes; you will see no mutilation of bodies here! Those who mutilate bodies have no respect for the dead, they act like crabs scrabbling in the tide. We have seen the mutilation carried out by Barbary raiders. The scars they leave are feeders on a map that can lead us back to their lairs; we will hunt them, just as we hunt the lobster before offering it the cooking pot.'

Cihtric put his hand upon a giant lobster from the table and began to tear it apart before turning to a warrior. 'The cage, what are we doing with the cage?'

'The baited cage awaits its lobster,' the warrior replied, making a scissor movement with his hands.

Once more Agen returned to the conversation and began probing. 'How do you manage your signals and deal with conditions like mist, night, storms?' he asked.

'Fire and the horn, what else do we need? Every port entrant is treated as an enemy and until the all clear is given we stand alert. The distance is too great to see a flag, in poor light perhaps we could use a pole … sound can travel this distance. You will see. The timing is very important since after a signal, an alarm, we have to cover a distance as does an enemy; distances and control points become training objectives. We train over these distances.'

'Is that why you have a hamlet called the sanctuary?' queried Agen.

'You'll see what the sanctuary is for; it's all connected to the chase and an ability to cover ground at speed.' Cihtric waved to a guard. 'So bring the Irish chieftain!'

At this request the feast room filled with warriors, some still exhausted from their exertions. These new faces were different from those of the clan leaders who had directed operations against the Irish. These were the men who had waited almost four hours in the dark before entering the corridor and the pits to kill those warriors still left alive. These men were accomplished with the bow and the spear; there was no delight on their faces. Sullen, shocked, they had met with the enemy and prevailed. Their eyes were sore from the smoking hay bales, sore from the long wait, unsure whether their graven opponents would revive and strike back.

These Winswood men had experienced death and they were not joking or laughing. Filling their mouths with mead or wine, they needed something to turn their minds away from the slaughter imposed upon the Irish enemy. There was no grasping for food, their stomachs showed no craving for the table's choicest dishes.

Something was needed to break the tension.

The Irish chieftain was brought in.

'Bring your champion, I'll fight any of your champions,' cursed the Irishman.

'You have fought our champions and lost. Your life is forfeit; there will be no further fighting of champions for you. However if you outrun our beast you might be set free. But first to remember us – bring in the beast,' ordered Cihtric.

'See that hamlet across the park? It must be a mile and a half.' Cihtric pointed. 'You will be set free and you must run for that hamlet; we call it the sanctuary. From there, if you reach it, you will be escorted to your ship. There are ten of you left. You have broken your promise to us and to your princess. She will be bonded over to Karl, our new tribute lord. You will have to entreat with him for her return. But first the beast.'

'Or shall we rip him apart with our horses?' asked Ryd. 'Where are my horses?' Two of Ryd's warriors jumped up and pretended to be horses ready to pull the Irishman apart.

The feast room warriors laughed and then hearing the beast immediately fell silent.

The most ferocious animal that looked as if it had been bitten in the head appeared with two keepers, slavering at the mouth; it was Ryd's striped hyena. Space quickly appeared around the animal.

Fearless in spite of this formidable animal the Irishman spoke:

'Consult and make your choice, horse or beast I'll engage your
    menace
In Kylgh perhaps every Saxon quakes
But soon you'll taste Gaelic fury
A curse on you and every member of your clan.

Why, even your hawks will flee their oaks.
Not one coin of the maiden's ransom will be paid!
My vision – Winswood dismembered
Your pagan gods sacrificed
Kylgh, animals, beasts, all in flames.

RELEASE ME!

I'm no Viking thrall
Your port will be tomorrow's secret
Cut, aborted, denied
There will be gullies, nay, leats of blood.

Your sanctuary, mothers, your children
Fired, charred, all will perish and your slaves
Ah, slave towns, I smell … sea
And men – they'll bathe in your port tonight
Beyond every buzzard's claw.'

'Enough,' shouted Cihtric. 'We won't see you again – so far you are unscathed but now you will taste our champion.'

The chieftain's arm was held towards the beast. A blood-curdling cry rent the air as the beast tore at the man's hand and his forearm. The chieftain dripping with blood was thrown into the park.

'RUN, RUN FOR YOUR LIFE!'

The handler looking at Cihtric waited for his order while the beast lapped at the blood.

At this spectacle several of the warriors refrained from shrieking for more blood; perhaps they had already seen too much blood.

'No,' shouted Cihtric, halting the handler from releasing the beast, 'let the Irishman complete his run. We'll save the beast for someone else – the locksmith. More wine, more wine – tether the beast outside, wait for the cage. The locksmith,' Cihtric sighed, shaking his head; he seemed reluctant to continue. 'Why has he appeared? Reader, why have you brought him to my attention?'

'He knows the labyrinth,' said the Reader, 'the treasure passage, the very soul of Winswood; one such man would be a great catch for those parties intent on the destruction of Winswood. If we are to make an example then he is a target. He knows of the treasure, he built all the cages, knows the passages.'

'But what has he done to deserve the cage?' queried Cihtric.

'The Duke suggested his name be brought to your attention,' said the Reader.

'The Duke … so the Duke wants him dead; well then whoever hits the rope with an arrow will despatch the cage to its destruction below and there the beast can gnaw on the bones,' said Cihtric.

'We too have tests of marksmanship; in our land an eagle's

feather is attached to a pole and whoever shoots the feather receives an honour,' remarked Agen.

'But not death, eh?' remarked Cihtric. 'It's another of our dishonourable customs.'

Fuelled by songs and alcohol, behaviour declined as the Cornish downed copious quantities of wine and mead. The locksmith's cage was left hanging outside the castle wall where Morwenna could see it trolling to and fro.

Lucco the Duchess's dwarf had been the only archer attempting to hit the rope. He was on his fourth cart of arrows and it appeared that the rope was impossible to strike when suddenly the dwarf pulled an arrow and, exclaiming, 'Collet's spinch,' released it directly into the heart of the locksmith to the absolute surprise of the entire company.

Agen was shocked. 'Why did that happen? Look, your men are in shock – that wasn't supposed to happen, was it? Why did you let him do that?'

Cihtric smiled. 'Folk cheat, he wanted the man dead – look, see, he is after the hat.'

The dwarf had climbed the rope and sliding down onto the cage plucked the hat from the dying locksmith.

Cihtric turned to Ryd and shouted, 'Cut the rope, cut the rope now.'

Ryd stepped forward to cut the rope, but the dwarf was quick and unseen leaped off the cage as it fell, the hat spilling into the air.

'Why?' asked Agen.

'I wanted Morwenna to believe that you were in the cage. The dwarf spoilt my play, there was no other way,' said Cihtric.

From Princess Morwenna's cell could be heard a great shriek.

'Hear her cry? She thinks you have plunged to your death.'

'You have unusual entertainment; might I ask if you have something special for me?' Agen queried.

'Only to honour our treaty,' said Cihtric.

Agen became more relaxed and embarked upon another subject. 'Signalling, we haven't spoken about it,' he said, diverting Cihtric from the treaty. 'Without early warning you would all perish. You just can't hold the necessary men at arms on permanent duty unless … unless you have a great treasure to pay for them.'

'That's why I wanted to build up our resources at the port; we need to increase our manpower at the port if we wish to reduce the need for the whole castle to react to general alerts,' said Ryd.

'As you say, with limited men at arms we need to consider our choices. You can see that we have men arriving all the time even though the battle is long over. These are our reserve, but it still takes too long to bring them into the action and relieve our battle forces. Our battle troops are here to feast; the reserves enable us to taste this luxury. But as you see we need some advantage like the corridor of death,' said Cihtric.

'The Romans entered a corridor of death in the Teutoburg forest against my ancestors. We still talk about the slaughter to this day,' remarked Agen, 'yet the Romans returned and eventually were victorious.'

'Because your tribes quarrelled,' said Cihtric.

'You also need luck,' added Ryd, 'and a sacrifice to attract good luck.'

'This sacrifice, this pagan pursuit, this violence I have not seen for many years,' said Agen.

'The violence halts the storm against us. We are but a small nation,' Ryd reminded him.

'Against the Saxons,' said Agen.

'But Karl has brought the Saxons to heel. They will pay tribute,' said Ryd.

'The Saxon will never heel,' said Agen. 'We Franks must stay vigilant; like yourselves we are watchful and have signals.'

'And intelligence, and weapons advantage,' said Ryd.

'A killing pit, a killing zone, a killing point,' added Cihtric.

'You need elephants in your animal park,' said Agen. 'I've seen one at court, a present to Karl from the Moors of Spain. They trample and put fear in folk; imagine an armoured elephant charging down your corridor of death!'

'Bring me one,' appealed Cihtric. 'If you baptise us and take away all our slaves we will need a herd to move the trade goods from the port to the castle.'

'May you never see a scared elephant; they can turn and destroy their own troops,' advised Agen.

'I favour bees and hornets,' said Ryd. 'If we could train them they would provide an equal menace.'

'With similar consequences to the elephant,' said Cihtric. 'Why, I have no wish to sting my forces out of existence. It would certainly make folk run up and down the corridor quicker.' He laughed and raised his glass in a salute.

The jovial feasting atmosphere continued with good humour and large quantities of mead and wine.

'We haven't spoken of the tribute necessary or the journey of your church,' said Agen. 'When Leo III is reunited with his church and seat in Rome—'

'He will demand a presence here,' interjected Cihtric.

'Transactions and trade will increase, you will be safer,' said Agen.

'A simple life will increase in complication,' said Cihtric. 'Once we are joined to another body and brain we are weaker.'

'But stronger if you unite in the one body,' added Agen.

'With the one brain – Karl's,' said Cihtric.

'This will be the test,' said Ryd.

'And the coin?' queried Cihtric. 'It's easy to change the head on a coin but will people accept the new head? We could have treated with the Mercian King Offa before his death in 796. And his son alive as ruler just 141 days – Ecgfrith – both Christians – we rejected their advances.'

'No one will care so long as they receive many coins and the coin retains its value,' offered Agen.

'And the spiritual message?' appealed Ryd.

'Of course, there you may have just one head – Pope Leo III,' said Agen.

'That's what will spoil this feast, minstrel,' concluded Cihtric.

'We will be overwhelmed by foreign crafts … and law, what of our law?' asked Ryd.

'Yes, land and our law have shaped our circle. The land changes with whoever retains title. Bodies will flow like the tide across this dragon land,' said Cihtric.

'But even you pagans don't cry over dead shells, just lost Welsh gold, Carmarthen gold,' added Agen.

Cihtric looked sternly into the minstrel's eyes as if something deeper had struck a note. 'Ryd, take our friend to the bathhouse and check that the Irishman is escorted to the port and embarks. The minstrel wants to view some treasure so show him our slave girls. Reader, cast your thoughts on the day's events.'

'You wish to view our luck?' asked the mystic. 'Then let's go below to the cage and check the body!'

As Cihtric and the Reader rose, further along the feast table a warrior with the name of Uffa lunged at Petra. 'Here, girl, where do you take that mead? Here, fill my tankard.' With that he grabbed the maiden and as she struggled to release herself from his grip he tore the shirt from her back, and as he threw her to the feast table a great gasp filled the room.

'What sign is this?' Uffa shrieked at the top of his voice.

The Reader pushed his way through the clan bodies to view the horrific injury. 'Let me see that,' he shouted.

Cihtric moved closer and heard the Reader's words and watched; the Reader's finger traced the scar across Petra's body; 'A great struggle, fire, fire everywhere, a monstrous injury!' And he drew in his breath to snarl. 'She is cursed, she bears Thor's lattice,' he shouted, and he drew his sword. 'See the broken ring of Thor!'

Before the Reader could act further, Gavin appeared. 'How can she be cursed? She was saved! Thor spared her, the lattice is Thor's protection, you old fool!' he shouted, and clasping Petra he hastened the slave away, looking searchingly for support at Cihtric.

'I warned you,' screamed the Reader after the fleeing pair, 'a foreigner would come and harm Winswood. It's her, she will fill the labyrinth with blood, that is no human, no one will be safe with her!'

Cihtric now in a huddle with his guards remembered Gavin's contempt for the Reader's winter explanation of the ice blade. 'To the cage.' Cihtric cursed and pushed his warriors aside. How many other secrets remained to be uncovered? Had the festive drink addled everyone's brain, including the Reader's?

When they arrived at the cage the locksmith's crumpled body lay inside but the dwarf had disappeared and the minstrel's hat was nowhere to be seen; someone had made off with the locksmith's head!

Part 4

The Wood Spirit

They stand by a boiling cauldron
And stir
One with blond hair and
One with hair jet black.

Footsteps

Back in her cell at Castle Winswood the princess was holding her head in her hands. 'Mercy, what have they done to him? I watched thinking I saw arrows appearing in the sky. The cage slowly turned. His cries of despair were too much to bear. I could no longer look. The Duchess's hawks witnessed all the hour's misdeeds.

'Oh, the crash still rings in my ears. Murderers! What do they imagine their Devil's Valhalla will offer? More of this! Will no one challenge the violence? Oh how I fear their footsteps!'

Much later she began to sing a mournful Celtic lament. At its conclusion she cried out in despair, 'Now there will be no escape,' and she threw off her rough covering and cowered naked beneath the cell window, her tears flooding over the cell floor. How could she follow the minstrel?

Meanwhile at the bathhouse Ryd and Agen had arrived from the castle.

'What is your favourite weapon, Agen?' asked Ryd.

'The word – and yours?'

'The lucky dart,' answered Ryd.

'Was that your dart strike on Princess Morwenna and the Irish?' enquired Agen.

'What are you suggesting?' asked Ryd, simmering.

'You brought her ashore; I learn from my sources that the gold convoy never arrived in Rome. Someone has the gold and it's not you; you have attracted the Irish wrath and perhaps Morwenna is merely a diversion, an unlucky choice for a dart,' needled Agen.

'I suppose you think I was trying to raise a little capital. After all as a weapons man I have no titles, rights, nothing. You think I persuaded the Viking that Morwenna was a good target?'

'You mock me, Ryd; what is the truth?'

'The truth is that had I not taken Morwenna from the galley she would have disappeared over the side – just a watery exclamation for the crabs.'

'Do you still have the Duke's ear, his trust?' queried Agen.

'This battle has cost much and delivered nothing,' admitted Ryd. 'Morwenna remains a problem; she is reason enough for the Irish to mount another attack.'

'You have our treaty; have you concerns with our treaty, Ryd?' asked Agen.

Ryd looked him in the eye. 'Every duke takes an oath, first that he is recognised by the clan, then that he will preserve our faith in the pagan gods – of which there are many. Only after this oath do his supporters pay him homage. Our oath could accommodate the Pope's church, but for how long will the Pope be prepared to accommodate all other faiths in Cornwall? I worry over the law that your church will at some point play with. How can we share our laws with the Pope? This is a recipe for conflict. Our reader advised us of a conflict, of a secret at the start of the year; I wasn't present but my brother warned me of a problem. The locksmith is dead. Does that mean that our problem has disappeared? Discontent will simmer with the introduction of the Pope's church and his men will meddle with our laws, and you ask me if I have concerns. I want to see the Duke and my family advantaged; if the treaty succeeds in guaranteeing such an advantage I will prove a friend of the treaty.' He halted, noticing the approach of Gavin. Gavin had arrived with Petra, still flustered from his encounter with the Reader in the feast hall. Mallor accompanied them a few steps behind.

'Here is my brother. See that Agen's looked after,' Ryd said, turning to Mallor. 'I must speak with my brother.'

Ryd took his brother aside into an adjoining passage, leaving Petra, who disappeared into the bathhouse whilst Mallor was addressed by Agen.

'So where are the treasure rooms?' Agen asked Mallor.

'No one is allowed – they are below. You enter the passage to the well. Down at the middle level you will find the animals: dogs, the beast, no one ventures there. You wouldn't return alive. Why do you ask?'

'I've heard, we have all heard of the great hoard at the Circle,' said Agen.

'It's come from years and years of shipwrecks all along this coast. If a ship is wrecked the contents will find their way here. Indeed it is a great hoard,' said Mallor.

'So how many treasure rooms exist?' Agen persisted.

'You should ask the locksmith or one of the masters. I heard you talking of the Pope and his law – there will never be any fairness for women whatever law is chosen,' said Mallor.

'Women only need laws if they own property, if they own commercial rights, if they exert influence.'

'In this land the priestesses still play a role. What will happen to them when your pope rules?' asked Mallor.

'The power of the priestesses and druids will end. The pagan religions will not be tolerated.'

'So our present powers will be depleted – this is a state that we will not welcome.'

'But you are but slaves, female slaves, and although you may hold trusted positions this will end. All slaves will be freed,' said Agen.

'And then who will look after us? I suppose you will herd us into monasteries; we will be like that Irish child Morwenna, delivered to the Pope!'

'There is no higher duty,' said Agen with a smile.

In the side passage the brothers were deep in conversation.

'I'm not going to the port,' said Ryd to Gavin. 'I shall check at the corridor to see that the Irishman has been led to his vessel. I feel uneasy; why did they rush the corridor? They had too few men to threaten Winswood. Our troops continue feasting and the reserves are slow to arrive; what can we do?'

'I'll arm the male slaves in the lower stockade, the slave town,' Gavin said. 'I'll tell my commanders that the slaves are to share in our feasting. We will trust them to carry weapons and we will observe their behaviour.'

'One hundred male slaves with weapons?' questioned Ryd.

'They know we have slave women too. They will not wish to run a risk with their young lives,' Gavin reminded him. 'When all the reserves arrive and complete our defence we will tell the slaves to stand down.'

'So be it, this will give us time. Keep your eye on the minstrel and return him to the castle,' concluded Ryd. 'Perhaps the Irish had no intention of storming the castle, perhaps all they intended was to raid the bathhouse hoping to find the Duchess or someone to exchange for Morwenna.'

'Whatever their mission, it failed,' said Gavin. 'We both love Winswood; long may it remain in our hands.' Gavin made no mention of Petra's uncovering at the feast.

Ryd departed; Gavin descended to the beast's cell and after a brief search turned to the duty guard with a message to inform his deputy Skalk to arm the slaves at the stockade. He then climbed the stairs to the bathhouse.

'Agen,' said Gavin, 'you need to view our girls; come, let's pass through to the main bath.'

'I'll stay long enough to bathe,' said Agen, 'but where are your giants? Dragons and giants I was promised in Paderborn.'

'Our giants are with the Duke in Bodmin at a wrestling contest. You'll prefer our girls to the dragons and giants,' said Gavin, and smiling they both entered the intimate atmosphere of the Winswood harem. Their bathing would soon be interrupted.

The bathhouse was arranged into a number of salons with separate bathing areas. In one of these facilities the black slave Kambon paga was alone sitting in the water naked. She was surprised by the arrival of Petra who cast off her clothing and joined her in the water. They were both alone.

Since neither could speak the other's language the young women settled to viewing each other's body. At first Petra could not see Kambon's back but on the front of her body from between her breasts to below her navel there were raised skin patterns in some strange directional design. Petra was captivated, and moving closer she slowly ran her finger over the design in a way so as not to give Kambon reason to fear her touch. As her finger traced the undulations she observed Kambon's eyes. Kambon's face had several markings but it was the cicatrisation between her breasts that continually attracted Petra's attention. Kambon looked deep into Petra's eyes; what did they both seek? At last she turned, yielding her back for view. Petra halted. These scars were different. First she noted recent wounding from the Welsh attack, then she noted another African form of scarification that counted the days, the journeys, stopping points, obstacles; this was a map for black slaves to find their way home.

In the space of several minutes Petra had carried out an intimate inspection of the young slave's body. Now Petra brought her own right arm up to touch her white left shoulder and, pointing, she turned in the water, enabling Kambon to view her back. No words came from the black slave's lips; just her black fingers were awake and they tracked the dragon-like coil that ran from Petra's left shoulder blade all the way down to her buttock. Then she returned as if riding the coil, as if on the bow wave of her own great river, the Niger. Right at the top of the shoulder blade the 'river' burst out into what seemed like hundreds of tributaries dispersing the coil across Petra's vertebrae right to the other side of her body. There was a fire colour in this pattern, hot and intense; how had Petra survived this ordeal? The black slave's fingers consulted the latticework; no language was necessary. Petra turned and both young women faced each other. Each trailed a hand in the water, each had a tear in the eye, and as their tears mingled in the water they shared each other's painful experience endured far back in the past.

Later, with their cheeks still wet from teardrops, their sad interlude was halted by the noise of company entering an adjoining facility. The weapons men were arriving. Another set of experiences could have awaited these young women new to the bathhouse. Instead the signal alarm and its mournful call set the bathhouse colony on full alert and returned the warriors to their stations.

Arrival of the Franks

The injured Irish chieftain had been delivered to the quay and immediately his remaining crew had set sail for Ireland. Navigating toward Lundy Island, far out of sight of the Kilkhampton shore, the Irish noticed a great fleet of ships off Lundy all flying a flag never seen before in these summer Atlantic waters.

'Look at all these ships, these must be the Franks – they arrive to support the Cornish,' said a sailor close to the Irish chieftain.

'We will bait them,' replied the chieftain; 'as we pass through, we will tell them the Cornish were defeated by the Saxons.' The chieftain began waving his injured arm. 'Lepers, we are lepers returning home, our freedom guaranteed by the Saxon victors, keep clear, keep clear. The Cornish are defeated. Beware the Saxon wrath.'

'Let them through,' said the Frank ship commander, 'do not touch them, we will check if the Saxons hold the castle when we reach port. Make speed; we have united our fleet off Lundy; we have little time to aid the Cornish if he speaks the truth.'

At Signal Point the Cornish signallers were merry. Challor and seven archers had left for the feast; just three signallers remained.

The Irish vessel with its chieftain had disappeared into the distance. 'He's gone,' young Wolf shouted, and then hardly an hour had passed with the signallers revelling in their mugs of mead when Wolf shrieked, 'I see more ships, three, ten, more, look, more, they are rowing towards us.' Horrified the signalmen leapt to their feet to view the presence of a massive fleet of foreign vessels heading for the port; the alarm horn was sounded. It was low tide, the rocks would be easily avoided. The signalmen feared that this fleet gently arriving on the fleeing tide could be connected to the earlier struggle; the dead Cornish guards from that attack had still not been replaced at the port.

Within the hour the invading Franks had organised their forces on the quay undisturbed by any Cornish guards.

The Franks disembarked and later that afternoon their warriors arrived at the lower ford crossing on the Coombe River. The Franks were unopposed and vessels full of troops and horse continued to arrive on the returning tide. Soon a thousand troops and horse commenced the march east towards Kilkhampton and the castle.

'Our men have found Saxons with weapons ahead,' said a Frank scout; 'hundreds are brandishing weapons and making a great deal of noise. It is as you suspected; the Cornish must have been overrun by the Irish with Saxon support, just as that sailor reported.'

The Frank commander shouted his orders, 'Push further up this road onto the Saxons, send scouts up that route to the right. If the route on the right is suitable for horse send up our horsemen behind the scouts and flank the Saxons in front. We need to bring our horse into play, you can't do that in a gully, and we need to break out, onto an expanse where we can use our strength. Our cavalry have never been beaten.'

'So, horse divert to the right and the foot tackle the Saxons head on? And what of the Cornish?' asked his deputy.

'Do you see any of them? Their port is deserted; perhaps we

will find what remains of their force by the dragon castle,' the commander replied. 'If not, the twenty men we sent to the signalling point on the cliff above to tackle the alarm should have reached that post by now; perhaps from there we will learn the fate of the Cornish.'

At Signal Point the signallers had lit all their fires and continued to sound their horn.

'Wolf helped light all the fires,' said Hud; 'our signal alerting the castle that the enemy has returned has prepared them for the next great battle – with such a fleet I fear for all our lives.'

'Their foremost troops will soon be at the ford and in front of the slaves at the stockade,' said Jard. 'We will fire our remaining arrows until the stocks are depleted, then retire to the choice and aid the slave attack; they will need our support.'

'Will we have time to escape?' queried the young boy called Wolf.

Jard took a long look at him, then looked to his horse. 'Take my horse, Wolf,' he ordered, 'make for the choice!'

Jard and Hud were left together on the cliff to release their arrows on the Franks still unloading men and weapons from the ships far below. But in the thirty minutes spent monitoring the disembarkation and aiming their arrows, the Cornish had been encircled.

'They are on us, it's too late,' shouted Jard, who with sword raised above his head rushed at the Franks. An arrow pierced his body, then with a single sword strike he was decapitated, his body tossed over the cliff. Hud suffered the same fate.

'It's a long drop,' said a Frank soldier gazing onto the rocks below. 'They lost their lives wanting to communicate our presence, yet we came as friends; these flags are Cornish, the Cornish beast – the boar – not Saxon, they misunderstood our intentions.'

'Why did they unleash their arrows at us?' asked his colleague.

'It's a mistake. There will be signalling mistakes like this, until people solve how to interpret signs correctly,' said a young Frank warrior.

'Look past the fires, can you make out the dragon castle?' asked another.

Peering into the distance the Frank group gasped at the sight of the great castle.

'There, it's there, the castle of death!'

An older warrior tore them away from their fixation. 'Don't extinguish these fires; let them burn. Better get back to the port; bring their flag, we couldn't see it from down below. Come, hurry, there's still time for more honours.'

Up at the castle the Duchess stood in a reception room, positioned at the window, looking towards Signal Point.

'Another sighting of enemy ships – it must be the Irish; where's Lucco? Until this Irish princess is dead we will have no safety at Winswood. How many fires are lit?' She tried to count the fires, then she turned towards her caged hawk. 'Ah, my little hawk, come take a flight, let's see what news you can bring me!' The Duchess released her hawk from the window. 'Taking this Irish maid in ransom was a dreadful mistake,' she added. 'Where, where has Lucco hidden the yew, the poison potion to despatch the girl?'

At this point Cihtric entered the reception room. 'My lady, we have—'

'I know, another alert, and how many fires?' she asked.

'It is a great fleet, we underestimated the Irish,' admitted Cihtric.

'And overestimated the support from Karl,' the Duchess added.

'You have reason to criticise; this matter has not brought security to Winswood, and then there is the matter with the Saxons – what should we have done?' Cihtric queried.

'The Duke concerns himself with the Saxons at Bodmin, the secret negotiations continue but as you know that's many miles from Winswood,' she replied. Only the Duchess and Cihtric had shared the Saxon secret.

Gavin and Ryd now appeared at the room door. Gavin on hearing the alarm at the bathhouse had returned Agen to his cell at the castle, much to the surprise of Morwenna. She had thought he was dead. Gavin had then proceeded to the Duchess's chamber where he had met Ryd.

'Father – excuse us, milady – we must head for the corridor, there is so little time,' said Ryd.

'I have settled the minstrel back in his cell, milady,' added Gavin.

'Then we must away, ma'am,' said Cihtric.

'And my dwarf, where is Lucco?' asked the Duchess.

'I … He was at the feast … I must away; keep to your rooms, for safety,' Cihtric replied.

The men now departed with the exception of Gavin, who lingered.

The Duchess returned to her window and the hawk that had been circling returned on her call. 'My pretty, I hear your sounds; we have waited and waited. But just a moment longer and if no good news strikes my ears, we will turn to the yew, but where is that dwarf?' she asked, returning the hawk to its cage.

'We can't wait for the yew,' interjected Gavin. 'We have spoken about Morwenna—'

'I thought the yew.' The Duchess seemed determined to administer a potion.

'Give her this – its Ryd's ring from the beast's cell,' said Gavin, thrusting the ring into the Duchess's hand.

'It's the ring of the Chatti!' she exclaimed. 'Ah … the ring with the pledge, I remember these rings from my childhood. You pledge over the ring to kill an enemy!'

'Then pledge to kill,' said Gavin. 'Give it to her!'

'Can we be sure of its force?' asked the Duchess.

'The force? Ryd's seen it work, he told me so,' said Gavin.

'Then it will be done – I cannot wait for Lucco; I will meet with Morwenna!'

Gavin left the room for the slave stockade and the Duchess prepared to meet Morwenna.

Battle for the Slave Stockade

Gavin was now stationed above the male slave stockade where his horse, spearmen and a few archers were the only troops between the Franks and Winswood. Skalk, Gavin's deputy, had returned on horseback to Gavin's position after reviewing the events at the slave stockade.

'The Saxon slaves fight bravely,' said Skalk; 'they fight for their lives. Weapons men, invaders are behind me – I took care to avoid our pits.'

'Send down our herds,' ordered Gavin, 'let our cattle descend on them, smash them to pieces; that will drive them back. Then they might seek an alternative – the corridor of death.'

Skalk ordered the herdsmen and women folk forward, pressing on a great herd of animals. 'It's done; let's see if this will bring us the respite we need.'

'How many men are we dealing with here?' asked Gavin. 'We need to reduce their numbers. We never considered an enemy would mount this route to Winswood. First they have fought their way past the stockade and now they climb the hill; let's see how they contend with this stampeding herd driven down upon them.'

'Some might flee the herd and steer further right towards the cliff farm,' replied Skalk; 'that route would bring them out high on the cliffs and sign them an alternative route from the port.'

'Their commanders will fear that route since they could be charged into the sea,' said Gavin. 'No, they will wait for the herd to pass and continue up towards us.'

'We are just 150 here, there are thousands down there,' said Skalk.

'If there are thousands down there I will call on my reserves to stiffen and block this route to Winswood. That will cause them to simmer in the cauldron by the slave stockade and enable our attack from the horsepark on the other side of the corridor to commence. At the choice, our signalmen will join the slave attack. We have perhaps one hour before we signal for our corridor archers to join us in front of Winswood,' replied Gavin.

'I hope you are right,' said Skalk. 'We are too few here to repulse a major attack.'

'It's time for our men to earn their honours. Send the archers forward and fire on any troops that evade the herd,' ordered Gavin.

'We still have no idea of the size of this new force,' said Skalk.

'No matter; if we divide them we can tackle each group, isolate and kill them,' said Gavin.

'They seem like ants – good that they can't bring any cavalry to bear on us from down there! But what are they?' queried Skalk, pointing at the cliff farm and mounted troops that had suddenly appeared.

'We have been betrayed,' spat Gavin, 'they have found their way up the cliff, they must have split their forces at the ford.'

'They split their horse from their foot force,' observed Skalk.

'Ryd always said we should increase our pits across the cliff farm … oh, if we had listened,' replied Gavin. 'Send in my cavalry,' he shouted, 'hit them now, don't wait for more to arrive.'

Fifty of the Cornish horse moved to oppose the Frank horse appearing on the cliff heights 400 feet above the sea at Stowe Farm.

'I can't wait to discover the outcome of this cavalry manoeuvre,' said Gavin. 'Send the signal to Ryd for the horsepark attack to commence.'

'It's done,' reported Skalk. 'Now we need the reserves up with us – we must defend against their cavalry. If we fail to hold them back well their main force will be upon us. It must be long past six o'clock … who will be alive at midnight?'

'See those flags,' exclaimed Gavin, 'they aren't Irish – they belong to the Franks!'

On hearing the horns from Signal Point the Cornish commanders had dispersed from the feast room and returned to the sanctuary end of the corridor of death.

'Good that we have our reserve troops directly in the corridor while Winswood retains our drunken army. I have drunk too much wine; they've caught us here … a shock landing in the night and now a full force this evening,' said Ryd. 'Nothing yet in the corridor, not even a sign of them,' he added.

'And your brother?' asked Cihtric.

'He armed the slaves down there at the stockade, they will be fighting for their lives,' he replied.

'Unless the foe are Saxon,' said Cihtric. 'We have no idea who comes against us. More Irish or—'and then suddenly they heard enemy horns.

'I haven't heard these battle horns before. I wonder if Gavin can see any flags, any battle standards,' mused Cihtric.

Cranock watching for a signal from the high field opposite shouted, 'A signal, a signal from Gavin … attack from the horsepark, he wants us to attack them in their rear at the choice, now!'

'Send in the herd from your side,' ordered Cihtric to

Cranock, 'push hard down on them, *block all corridors from the cauldron*. Find them and trample them.'

'And what if they come in thousands?' asked Ryd.

'What, one hundred ships?'

'Listen to the signal blasts! See the fires! It's an endless horde!' Ryd shouted.

Ruan the teller joined the group and announced, 'They are Franks!'

'Impossible,' replied Cihtric. 'They are our friends.'

'I was with your son on the Weser, I heard these battle sounds, they are Franks I tell you,' said Ruan.

'Father, your signals have no way of splitting friend from foe! If they see Saxons with swords they will think ...' Ryd couldn't finish his reply.

'That Winswood was overrun by Saxons,' interjected Cihtric.

'How long can we sit here?' asked Ryd. 'If Gavin has signalled from his position he must have seen the Franks along the cliff or up past the slave stockade. He needs us with him!'

'It's true we must withdraw to Winswood,' said Cihtric. 'It's too late to join Gavin. The corridor is dry! We need to kill some of their army to reduce the pressure. Why didn't they attack us in this corridor – are they advised by the Irish?'

'I warned you about that cliff side, we needed pits,' Ryd answered.

'The Duke wouldn't authorise construction, just a few up by the stockade but none on the cliff path,' replied Cihtric.

'The Duke should be here to share our predicament,' Ryd said, filled with scorn.

'Send a message to the Duke,' ordered Cihtric.

'I will see to it,' said Ryd, and he called for two messengers.

'Then meet me at the castle,' called Cihtric as he mounted his horse and rode for the castle.

Ryd turned to Ruan. 'Cranock with our remaining men will cover the corridor; you, Ruan, take fifty men and support the herd at the choice.' Then Ryd raised his voice. 'Where are my riders?' he shouted just as two horsemen arrived. Leaving Ruan to carry out his instructions he turned to the riders. 'I pass you two messages. This one is for the Saxons at Clovelly – tell them their enemies the Franks are at Winswood. This other message is for the Duke at Bodmin – tell him he will find our bodies at the castle – the Franks are attacking over the cliff path and not through the corridor!'

The riders rode away on their missions while Ryd set off for the castle.

In Morwenna's cell at the castle the Duchess, somewhat agitated, approached the princess, whose demeanour had recovered slightly now that Agen had been returned to his cell.

'Wear this ring, child, a charm, it will offer you the protection you wanted,' said the Duchess as she offered the ring to Morwenna.

'Will my finger blacken?' asked Morwenna.

'See, wear it like this.' The Duchess slid the ring onto her second finger, showed it to Morwenna and then slowly removed it. 'See, it hasn't left a mark. The armies press, you need a charm, child.'

'I have my faith,' Morwenna reminded her, 'but if you feel I need a charm, well, I will wear it!' She busily inspected the ring and slipped it onto her middle finger.

The Duchess reassured Morwenna, tapping her hand. 'Now, child, I must hurry for the bathhouse, I need to attend to the little grey stallion – Tamar. If I find my dwarf Lucco I will send him to comfort you.' Then she turned and left the cell, leaving the guard to lock the door and return to his post at the end of the passage.

Aware that the guard had departed, Agen called to Morwenna. 'You said the locksmith wanted us to loosen a stone.'

'I did, this one, my buckle presses against the loose stone, see,' she replied.

They both began to agitate the stone until it became dislodged, leaving Agen able to open the door between the two cells. Within minutes he had broken into Morwenna's space.

'Agen, I'm so afraid,' cried Morwenna.

'Call the guard, I will hide behind the door and overpower him,' said Agen.

It took some minutes before Morwenna was ready to call the guard, she had been so traumatised by the day's events. 'Guard, guard,' called Morwenna.

'What is it, what is it?' called the guard, hurrying along the corridor from where he had been sitting.

'See from my window, an army attacks.' Morwenna pointed.

The guard rushed to open the door and see for himself; he was hit and knocked unconscious by Agen.

'Come – leave him, he won't come round after that,' shouted Agen. He grabbed the guard's weapons and scurried along the passage with Morwenna.

Just a few minutes later Cihtric arrived in the castle and began preparations to meet the Franks.

'I'll check the tower cells,' said Cihtric to himself; 'perhaps it's not too late for me to stir Agen to call a halt to this madness, unless the Franks really have joined with the Irish!' Arriving in the cell passage he could not find the guard; he rushed towards Morwenna's cell. 'They are gone. Where are they?' Cihtric shouted.

Inside he heard the groaning of the guard recovering from Agen's battering. 'I was struck … it must have been the stone,' said the guard.

'Get to the battlements, get some weapons,' cursed Cihtric, ordering the guard away and moving quickly to the cell window. He looked out in the evening light and saw a mounted army lining up ready to face Winswood. 'We are too few,' acknowledged Cihtric, and he left the passage for the battlements.

The Labyrinth

The labyrinth held Winswood's treasure and to ensure that the treasure remained safe the passages to the treasure rooms were linked to the wild animal chambers. With torches lit the labyrinth throbbed with a dull red glow; this was no place for those not familiar with the passage layout or the feeding habits of the animals. Attached to the labyrinth were the castle stables and it was this address that claimed the Duchess's attention. Tamar the young grey stallion from the Weser had occupied the Duchess's thoughts ever since his arrival. Now just after delivering a death ring to the Irish princess the Duchess had decided to lance another problem – to ensure the purity of her herd of blue horses Tamar had to be eliminated.

She entered the stable and moved cautiously toward the young animal; as soon as Tamar nudged her hoping for a treat the Duchess drew a short dagger from her cloak and plunged it into the horse's neck. There was a spurt of blood and the animal collapsed to the floor. The Duchess crouched close to make sure that the stallion had indeed taken its last breath. Blood coursed across the stable floor and over the Duchess's hands and cloak. She smeared her hands seeking to free them from blood, then decided to cross the passage to the bathhouse to effect a better cleansing process. It was at this point that she became aware that someone or something else was running through the labyrinth. She waited several minutes; should she hide? Was it the beast? Then from a long passage that led towards the slave stockade Gavin appeared.

Before she could hide from Gavin he was upon her. 'What

is this?' he cried. 'What madness has overcome you? Blood, you are covered in blood!'

The Duchess dropped her dagger and fled toward the bathhouse.

Gavin halted for a moment unsure of what had taken place, then, aware that he did not want to meet with the beast, he pursued the Duchess along the passage to the bathhouse.

Inside the bathhouse Mallor was reassuring the slave girls. 'There is no need to panic,' she said. 'It's true a great battle must be raging but we withstood the earlier battle. Why consider that we should fail in this one?'

'And what is she doing here?' shrieked Petra, seeing Morwenna approaching with Agen.

'Morwenna insisted she would not leave the castle until I promised to bring her here,' interjected Agen.

'These slave girls must be saved,' shouted Morwenna. 'All is lost, the Cornish will kill you. You must all come with me, now! See …'

Morwenna was horrified; standing before her was the Duchess covered in blood.

For a moment the Duchess halted, then she moved slowly towards Morwenna who shrieked, 'What pagan message is this? What have you done? I'll have no more of your ring.' Stripping the ring from her finger with a move bringing her hands above her head, Morwenna dropped to her knees and let the ring spill in front of Petra. 'Save me, Lord,' implored Morwenna.

Petra picked up the ring and examined it. 'A Chatti ring. I know this ring, the ring with the pledge.' She inhaled violently, showing her teeth; something from long ago jogged her memory. Dropping the ring as if under a spell, she drew a hidden blade from her robes, then snatching and holding Morwenna's hair she drove the blade deep into the princess's neck. '*Sterbe!*' she screamed, withdrawing the bloody blade. Blood spurted from the wound, splashing all over Petra onto the floor.

Gavin, seeing the strike blade drive home, froze to the spot; this was an exact rendition of the beheading scene acted out in his vision on his journey to the Weser! He held his sword above his head as if trying to protect himself from some evil threat that had broken free and gained control of the Duchess and now Petra.

'She's dead! What is there to fight over?' snarled Petra. She waved the bloody dagger aloft.

Gavin gasped, 'Huuuu!'

No one was moving, each looked for support from another; what had they witnessed? Still holding his sword Gavin grabbed Petra.

'Give me the sword,' ordered the Duchess. 'Gavin, give me your sword now,' she shrieked, and she moved toward Gavin and Petra.

'You shall have my sword,' said Gavin and he plunged the sword right through the Duchess's body, killing her almost instantly. The Duchess gave a dying gasp and collapsed to the floor.

Mallor and all the slaves screamed in terror; Agen leaped to the princess's side, cradling her head in his hands. 'Morwenna, Morwenna,' he repeated. But he could do nothing.

Gavin led Petra towards the labyrinth, through to the passage by the well stairs. 'Come, come quickly, we must away,' he said to Petra.

The Arab wail and Mallor's screams punctuated their departure. Only Kambon was silent and her eyes fixed upon the Chatti ring discarded by Petra. Seizing her opportunity, in the blink of an eye she scooped it up from the blood-drenched floor and closed her hand over its dark force.

Hurrying down the stairs Gavin urged Petra forward.

'She had to be killed,' said Petra. 'I knew if Morwenna appeared in the bathhouse she was to be killed; didn't you plan it that way? That ring harbours a death pledge!'

'This was not the plan, Petra!' Gavin lied; how could he forget the scene, with Morwenna's raised hands, and Ryd's ring demanding death? 'Neither did I plan to kill the Duchess,' he added.

Gavin led Petra down the escape route towards a knot of corridors controlled from the beast's cell. Petra could see how this cell controlled the escape route. Gavin left an interconnecting door open. The beast must still have been busy in the castle park with its keeper. Now with its cell door wide open Petra and Gavin would need to be quick in the tunnel.

The corridor and escape routes below ground were every bit as dangerous as those above. The full extent of Winswood's evils barely spoke out in the light that shone from the two torches. This far down there were few cells with darker secrets. An evil stench filled the air, an unseen witness to the decay and putrefaction that seeped into the main corridor.

Fear was triggered everywhere you looked. The moment you moved underground you became a target – if not the beast something else would stalk you. This was the rule of the labyrinth. If you had no business here, no right to roam, you would be hunted. The light from the torches illuminated each cell, each corner, and a story emerged. Lepers forgotten. Prisoners forgotten. Everywhere rush. As your feet struck fresh rush stems, there would be an ominous crack to alert the beast. In any instant you could be ambushed.

Somewhere in this maze was the great treasure hoard. The locksmith had worked for years; he had seen silver and gold enough for a king's ransom. More cartloads than the Avar treasure!

If there were sounds you stopped and listened. Dripping? There had been something here long before the hill had been shaped by human hand. Something deep. Something earlier. Something that needed to be hidden. All the time your mind was occupied by a current stimulus – a sound. Behind each sound lurked a feeder, a link to an older influence and influence from an earlier distraction at Winswood, something from a buried layer. You could not hide from this ancient influence; nothing could be hidden. The old evil was ready to be uncovered but Petra and Gavin had no time; they were running from the beast, trying to avoid anything that could hamper their progress and their escape.

'Be quick or the beast will find us and I have no interest in spending time fighting off that animal, but stop, let's see if Agen follows …'

They waited a moment in the passage, listening.

'Why don't you alert the beast?' said Petra. 'Let the beast deal with the minstrel!'

They were interrupted; it was Agen's call.

'No time,' said Gavin, and they returned to their descent of the passage.

After some time they reached the grills of a door that peered out to the sky. 'This passage brings us out through undergrowth to the rush, but you must be quiet,' said Gavin, 'the Franks are everywhere!'

'The Franks,' gasped Petra, and she looked up towards the

grill. There was a hat, she caught a glimpse of a minstrel's hat. As she cried out in surprise Gavin halted from putting out his flaming torch. Then in full view they both saw Lucco loading a stone slab onto the grill while flicking down on them what appeared to be ticks from his clothing. He muttered, 'Bretter's dust from a highlands pillow.'

'No,' shouted Gavin but it was too late.

Petra noted Lucco's face contorted with anger. He had closed off their escape route; there was no alternative but to move back up the labyrinth and contend with the beast or continue round the passage and hope to find another way out.

Gavin's throat was parched. He flicked off the ticks that had been thrown at them. 'I'm thirsty,' he said.

'Here, drink this,' said Petra, offering a water gourd.

'Where did you find that?' Gavin asked.

'I suppose it was left by Lucco, by mistake,' said Petra.

Gavin shook his head. The torch picked out their dilemma.

'Have you been here before, Petra?' asked Gavin.

'Of course not,' said Petra.

'Well, follow me,' said Gavin, and they continued along the passage, Gavin brushing at the ticks as they followed the light of his single remaining torch.

'The Reader thinks you are cursed, Petra,' said Gavin.

'The Duchess didn't think so,' she countered.

'I know,' said Gavin. 'We will soon be in the Duchess's secret room.'

'And what is that?' asked Petra.

'The room of heads,' said Gavin. And as the passage turned north towards the direction of the corridor of death Petra seemed more and more reluctant to follow.

'We'll soon be there,' Gavin said, 'just a few more steps,' and at last they came into a cavernous room. This room triggered in Gavin memories of the great hall at Verden.

'Look up, Petra,' he said, and in the ceiling everywhere poking down on them were inverted human heads. You could make out ears. Who were these people, the ear people? Other properties like eyes and mouths were just too difficult to identify.

'This was one of the Duchess's special projects,' said Gavin. 'She thought we didn't know about it but the locksmith told us. You were here, Petra. When the Duchess came down here she would have shown you this room. And you were here with her, weren't you?' he probed.

Petra was silent, viewing the heads.

'And do you know what can be found below this room?' he persisted. 'Let me tell you. Those who fall down here fall into a chamber where two executioners work. They stand by a boiling cauldron and stir, one with blond hair and one with hair jet black. They have pelts across their shoulders. They are pagan and wait for new bodies to process. The decapitated heads are for this room, special body parts like penises for the cauldron, the remaining flesh and bone is fed to a beast.'

Petra remained silent.

'They are waiting right now, aren't they?' He waited for Petra to reply, then spoke again when she did not. 'You probably know their names; listen, you can hear them.'

She was motionless, her face lit by the flickering torch, the water bag slung over her shoulder. Then she smiled laconically. 'You seem to know everything, Gavin.' She took a breath and shook her head sadly.

'I realised something was wrong when the ticks seemed to pass right through your body. You had no fear of them,' said Gavin. 'It was you who followed me in Verden. It was your footsteps that gave away your presence in the great hall. Your footsteps smeared blood across the floor. Look, even now your feet are covered in blood.'

Petra looked down and indeed her little feet looked as though she had been padding through a corridor filled with blood.

'The Reader was correct,' continued Gavin. 'You are not human; you can disappear at will just as you did in Verden; you're cursed!'

Before Gavin could add another word Petra said, 'So why didn't you give the Duchess your sword? She might have struck me.'

'The Duchess couldn't kill you, Petra. She indulged you, welcomed you into her secret society. She could have chosen Morwenna's head to add to her collection *or* mine. Of the two possibilities the latter course carried a higher risk for me.'

Petra pawed at Gavin, provoking him with her version of the beast's laugh.

Gavin stepped back toward the centre of the room where the great floor cavity waited.

'Here it is, Petra.' He pointed. 'Down there are your executioners, the pair of them. If their hands could only get through the bars of their cell they would pull me down. But you are protected. You have Thor's lattice. Thor's broken ring, and now it's a broken charm. We have discovered who you are.'

As if by magic Petra seemed to be growing in size, growing in front of him. Or was the ceiling of inverted heads descending towards him? He began to feel faint. He needed to prop himself up. He wanted to reach the walls. Instead he looked up and Petra was standing over him drinking from the water gourd. The potion splashed over his face, he shrieked and she was gone, hurtling down inside a spinning red tower. Gone forever. Or was she? What had happened? He couldn't see her footprints.

Flames from the torch he had dropped set fire to the rush. He had no time to look into the depths of the tower to see where Petra had landed. He smeared what remained of the wet potion from his face and looked up. The heads were agitated; they couldn't escape the flames or the choking smoke. They couldn't speak. Who could speak for them and each family's suffering? Names began to eerily fill the air. The room was soon a raging inferno. Gavin held a hand to his ear to shield him from the torrent of names being screamed at him. He stumbled; there right in front of him was the head of the locksmith! He screamed and grasping what remained of his burning torch he fled for his life down the nearest passage, hoping it would bring him out by the stables and return him to the castle.

Back along the passage Agen had given up calling Gavin.

While Gavin had known the beast was near and would be prowling the corridors Agen had backed up along the labyrinth, every turn in the underground corridor as troubling as the corridor of death above. It was only as Agen came to the stall where Tamar had been kept that he halted in horror; here he found the beast gnawing at the bones of the young stallion. Holding his burning torch aloft while the beast continued its grim work on the stallion's bones, Agen ran for the stairs and was confronted by the black slave who was peering down the stairs wearing just a sarong. As the torch picked out her features the girl cried out, hoping the man would recognise her. 'Kambon paga!' She had been on her way to the beast's cage to return the Chatti ring to its hiding place.

'This darkness is only for the beast,' Agen reassured her. 'But what are you holding?' he asked, noticing something tightly gripped in her left hand.

Kambon opened her hand to reveal the bloodied Chatti ring.

'I'll have that,' Agen snapped, snatching the ring from her grasp. 'Come, let's return to the light; I must return to the castle.'

She turned and Agen had a view in the torchlight of the scarred back of the slave with a map to the city of African gold.

On the battlements of Castle Winswood, Ryd had joined Cihtric.

'We are lost,' Cihtric said. 'Look, they swarm everywhere; not even Agen the minstrel could save us. We've killed many of their troops but nothing can stop them. Look at their numbers, thousands and not one came up the corridor of death!'

'It is too late to think of our mistakes,' said Ryd. 'We might still come out of this.'

'With our heads? The wine is still running around mine,' said Cihtric as he unleashed another arrow into the attacking Franks.

'The princess, the minstrel?' queried Ryd.

'Gone.'

'Ah, that minstrel!' exclaimed Ryd.

'Ah, that maid – you didn't tell me,' remarked Cihtric.

'Tell you what, Father?' replied Ryd.

'You didn't tell me that you and the Vikings had plans for the gold galley off Lundy,' answered Cihtric.

'The gold galley chose to throw Morwenna overboard. I was not a party to their plans,' swore Ryd.

'Indeed ... so while waiting on the treasure ships, the Dolaucothi gold mine ships from Carmarthen you knew nothing? The Vikings took the gold – and you were left with the maid!' said Cihtric.

'Aye, 'tis true,' said Ryd. 'She was on the treasure ship bound for Rome. She came aboard in Carmarthen and then sailed with the gold fleet for Lundy.'

'And your part of the treasure was the ransom! No wonder the Franks are upon us! And not one cartload of treasure for our hoard. All of it taken by the Vikings ... your friends.'

'I'm sorry, Father,' said Ryd.

Looking over the battlements Cihtric shook his head in displeasure. Then he noticed someone familiar wearing Agen's minstrel hat.

'I saw the dwarf, I heard ... hawk's chin—' began Cihtric, but before Cihtric could finish his sentence an arrow pierced his throat and he fell to the ground. 'I saw a beast,' he choked, 'Ryd, the curse, it's Petra, the Reader said she was cursed, her back!'

Ryd sought to aid his dying father but he could do nothing. The arrow had taken his life.

The battle continued to rage and to Ryd's surprise Agen appeared.

'Your father?' Agen asked.

'He's dead, I think the dwarf shot him,' sobbed Ryd. 'Father mentioned something about Petra.'

'We must stop this slaughter, this mistake; fly this – fly this from the mast,' said Agen.

'Surrender?' questioned Ryd.

'Surrender and live,' said Agen. 'You see this ring?' and he brought the iron ring from his pocket. 'Your brother watched his Saxon slave murder Morwenna. Then he plunged his own blade into the Duchess. She's dead. You know what that means for you and your family?'

'Death,' pronounced Ryd. What had his father said about Petra? Petra had now murdered Morwenna! And the beast? This he would keep to himself; it could only refer to an answer Cihtric had given to the Druid oracle at the 'waterfall of tears' before passing over some coins.

'You must act swiftly,' said Agen. 'Take the ring, perhaps the ring has worked its final piece of menace, tell the Duke, acquit yourself with the Duke and I will halt this battle.'

Ryd withdrew to one of the castle's chambers and gazed at the iron ring; what should he do? Did the ring hold the key to his future? Holding the ring, looking over its markings, he reflected on Ingvar's finger tracing a slave's back on the trail to Sijilmasa, and the blood map carved to show her way home. That slave Kambon cicatrised his memory; it was as if she had left the bathhouse and was walking naked towards him; this was the force the ring had unleashed, this was the way to freedom, he needed the African gold.

Without any further deliberation, Ryd returned to the battlements. To his aide he said, 'Ride with three of my men, take this ring to the Duke, tell him his wife perished in the battle – she was wearing this ring. Give him the ring, suggest he wear it in memory of the Duchess, for victory.' The warrior departed and Ryd added, 'I will become the hawk's chin.'

A hawk screamed overhead as the aide disappeared. The hyena was heard laughing in the park.

'I found Mother,' Gavin said with a whitened face as he joined the others on the battlements. 'She whispered Lucco's name with her dying gasp; I think he poisoned her.'

Ryd was dark as thunder; the dwarf was in the mix in the killing of both his parents.

'The dwarf counted the suffering too, each one had a given name.' Gavin was shaking. 'He mapped out all of the heads, the Duchess's gallery of heads, he hid the locksmith's head there too!'

'Cut off his head!' A shout was heard from below. Whose head?

Before Ryd could react Agen restrained him from looking over the battlements to see who had shouted. Agen was hardened to revelations about heads. 'Ryd, you have little time,' he interjected, drawing Ryd further away from Gavin. 'The white flag of surrender flies over Winswood, the Frank warriors have ceased to fight. Ryd, if the ring fails, you could be hanging from a rope or, worse, thrown to your beast! I have experienced the beast!'

'The ring won't fail, said Ryd; 'the Duke won't arrive at Winswood.'

And it was an accurate prediction; the Duke returning in haste from Bodmin set the ring on his finger before reaching Bude. Then, after a short halt at Stratton and between the Stowe cliff and the slave stockade, they say he was thrown from his horse. He died before he could enter Castle Winswood. The ring was lost.

Both brothers had made a sacrifice; Ryd had succumbed to the dark ring of the Chatti, Gavin thought he had grasped a new light. Ryd was declared Duke of Cornwall just in time for the swallows to fly south and bear the news – before October's winds shook and whisked all the leaves from the Winswood trees. Agen discouraged any talk on heads and headless bodies, the gallery of heads was covered up and all the treasure extracted. All entrances to the labyrinth were sealed. They say a woman's ghost frequents the hill: the ghost of Morwenna, or Petra, or the Duchess, perhaps Cihtric's wife or one of the many heads displayed in the gallery. It's certainly a ghost, which tunes to a monstrous event and a terrible suffering.

To be continued: Ryd of Winswood, Duke of Cornwall 799 AD – Return of the Giants.

Questions on the Text

1. Sir Richard Burton in his travel memoirs reported that to preserve them from being kidnapped, Meccan children on the fortieth day after birth were scarred on the face with three parallel gashes down each cheek. This practice of facial scarring migrated to some tribes of the River Niger. In Part 1 of the text Ingvar suggests that scars on the slave girl's back are a map to the city of gold. What is a more likely interpretation?

2. In Part 2 the interpretation of marks and features is extended. Can we gain an insight into the author's view of the practice of divination from a blade of ice?

3. Albert Camus wrote a poem called *The Massacre at Verden*. For Kynge the massacre is the 'incredible event' that drives his novella. What method of resonance does the author choose to reflect on the event and what character choices are made to illustrate his views?

4. One of the greatest problems a nation state faces is how to recognise a friend. We are all interpreters, Kynge says: some are silent, some prefer argument, some favour action; there are always consequences. At the sleeping beauty's castle in Germany close to the Diemel and Weser rivers, Sababurg Castle, the ruling family failed to recognise a witch. Castle Winswood and its sleeping beauties failed to recognise a friend! Why might Cihtric have had difficulties in recognising a friend?

5. The author 'channels' the methodology of 'Act, Vision, Provocation and Trust' to uncover a suffering, a complaint. Can you find examples in each part that might validate this proposition?

6. The author has chosen a jigsaw pattern on some of his visuals and in the book cover maps. 'The jigsaw is an interpretation of someone's view, a visual display of a problem; the pieces are laid out and you begin to make a map. Borders are filled, hot spots become a magnet, there is always a moment, 'the rush', when the jigsaw hastens towards completion and the problem's solution.' Discuss with reference to the text.

7. If the author has been 'channelled', is the communicator's intent to express a complaint about the migration of European Union laws to the UK and is the result a satire on German, particularly EU, justice?

8. In Part 4 Ryd invokes the power of the ring; would you have acted in the same way considering the circumstances of Ryd's 'no-win' situation?

9. Karl's version of Christianity is different from our modern concept of obliging peaceful co-existence of all faiths: discuss.

10. If you were to visit Kilkhampton in North Cornwall where could you stay and what other visual opportunities in the area would recommend a visit?

11. One of the author's mottoes is 'share your problem, don't own the problem'. If there was a curse on castle and clan how has it affected the prosperity and development of modern Kilkhampton? What measures are needed to lift the 'curse' and attract investment into the town?

12. Duchess Gisela struggles with the guilt of surviving the Irminsul destruction and avoiding the Verden Massacre; how can she administer justice in an unbiased manner if this psychic disturbance accompanies her? Does your answer provoke any considerations for examining the suitability of appointments to a modern judiciary?

Meet the Author

You say you want to see *The Legend of Castle Winswood* as a film?

That's correct; I always planned to make a movie of the legend. In fact I had three movies in mind: *The Legend of Castle Winswood, Ryd of Winswood, Duke of Cornwall 799 AD – Return of the Giants*, and *Tarmint from Fox*. The last is a modern film dealing with the disappearance of a website greeter.

Do you have anyone in mind for the parts in the first film?

I've paid attention to the career of Evan Rachel Wood, who I first imagined as Petra. Then I saw Evan in *Mildred Pierce* and knew immediately that she would make a fabulous Duchess of Cornwall. The character I had in mind has a strong face, with authority, almost like Cruella in *101 Dalmatians*; that's the face I am looking for.

How about music? I believe you have an artist in mind.

That's right. I loved Birdy's first album – the song that begins 'Smeared black ink' resonates with me, *The District Sleeps Alone Tonight*, love it! She has a very busy programme but I asked her to consider writing a lament for the ransom princess that captures Princess Morwenna's predicament at Castle Winswood.

My son Richard was 17 when he wrote and played the guitar solo for the YouTube location video we shot introducing the castle. My daughter Charlotte did the voice-over on that.

You've used the flying buzzard motif in your cover and maps.

That's right, how could I not include one of the stars of the story? That buzzard was an essential experience for me. I hope it is still flying and providing the inspiration that I enjoyed. The shrieking buzzard I have only experienced at Kilkhampton. I have it on video – awesome. Buzzards don't communicate like that in Hampshire, not with me!

Whilst the public footpath allows admittance to the Norman castle the site of Winswood Castle is behind private gates.

Yes, some years ago I was able to walk on the site and of course there is nothing left now; the old 60s Ordnance Survey maps show the castle site but on new maps it is no longer recorded. The road to the castle was marked as Chings Lane on a 1690 map. That has been removed, just like the castle, but that fits well with my story, hence Castle Winswood; it's my castle, in my imagination. However, if you climb Steeple Point or visit the Norman castle and look towards the trees of Winswood, this castle will appear for you too – try it! You will find that it fits well with a sleeping beauty castle like that at Sababurg in Germany, brought once more to life after a long sleep!

I don't recommend climbing Steeple Point in the wet; you need a safe dry day and close attendance to the dangers of cliff edge proximity, but the view from there will place you in no doubt that a castle existed. I am going to tell the story of its disappearance in the second book.

And you contend that below the bathhouse, your ladywell, there was a gallery, a gallery of heads?

That's right. If you observe similar structures like Burg Desenberg in Germany, miners worked on creating a gallery to locate a water source. One day they may unearth a gallery here. We know there is a water source and Cornwall is renowned for its miners.

What did you see when you viewed Lundy Island from the 'waterfall of tears'?

I saw a ring, it was a clear day, and no one stood to collect coins and pop a question.

Does the ring that put Ryd in a no-win situation exist?

It's lost somewhere around Kilkhampton; it says so in the book!

Finally, who would be most surprised to hear that you had written a book?

Richmal Crompton the author; she was a celebrity client on my car cleaning round as a teenager. Also Jack Abby of the Dale Martin wrestling promoters; I cleaned his wife's sports car. It would have been helpful to have discussed Cornish wrestling with Jack for my next book *Ryd of Winswood, Duke of Cornwall 799 AD – Return of the Giants*.

Acknowledgements

A big 'thank you' to Miles Bailey at The Choir Press in Gloucester. When I discussed my manuscript with Miles he checked on the 'massacre at Verden' and when I plugged into his reference an Albert Camus poem appeared. So I am not the only writer who was directed to this monstrous crime. My starting point, feeling in the dark, back to the fury and the incredible event was different. The numbers 1555 and 5555 now trigger for me a tale of unimaginable horror – a true corridor of death. Consider the single day's death toll at Verden for failure to convert to Christianity in AD 782 with the 20th century Jewish holocaust perpetrated by the Nazis and Stalin's communist blood letting. We have encountered a formula for human suffering – when do we react – who notices the 'pass words'?

Special thanks to my editor Harriet Evans and to Rebecca Love for her photographic input. Finally my 'jigsaw lead' would never have been completed without the support of Optimus, Sharki, Scout, Pancho and of course Monkey.